S0-AEO-773

THE UNITED STATES

— VS —

PVT. CHELSEA MANNING

A GRAPHIC ACCOUNT FROM INSIDE THE COURTROOM

THE UNITED STATES

— VS —

PVT. CHELSEA MANNING

CLARK STOECKLEY

ADDITIONAL TEXT BY MAX THORN

DESIGN AND LAYOUT BY SOMERSET BEAN

O/R

OR Books

New York · London

Published by OR Books, New York and London
Visit our website at www.orbooks.com

First printing 2014

Cataloging-in-Publication data is available from the Library of Congress.
A catalog record for this book is available from the British Library.

ISBN 978-1-939293-27-5 paperback
ISBN 978-1-939293-28-2 e-book

This book is set in Heavy Mettle, Self Destruct Button, Creator Credits and Arial.
Typeset by Somerset Bean.
Printed by BookMobile in the United States and CPI Books Ltd in the United Kingdom.

Preface

It's no easy thing to produce a book like this about the trial of Chelsea Manning.

The trial was conducted in unprecedented secrecy, as the Center for Constitutional Rights asserted, "far more...than even the prosecution of the alleged 9/11 plotters in Guantanamo." It is only because of the work of people like Clark Stoeckley and Alexa O'Brien that we can begin to appreciate what has happened. These pages are a precious window into that court room, and that serious historical event.

For the people who attended the trial, and for the people who watched from afar, it was an intense period. Chelsea Manning's trial continues to haunt us. The story is emblematic of the pressing political issues of our time, and the subject of deeply personal experience for so many.

It is a tall order to capture all of this in a graphic novel, but Clark, Max and Somerset Bean have done it. The drawings are expressive and haunting. The court transcripts come alive on the page. They bear powerful witness to the trial of America's foremost political prisoner.

Manning's significance as a prisoner of conscience is appreciated around the world. One day, it will be fully recognized in her own country, and her persecution will come to an end.

Free Chelsea Manning.

Julian Assange
London, March 2014

WikiLeaks
TOP SECRET
Mobile Information
Collection Unit
RELEASE
BRADLEY
MANNING
BRADLEYMANNING.ORG

Foreword

On April 5, 2010 I was editing a vast collection of what have come to be known as "war porn" videos for my MFA thesis exhibition. Disturbing footage from the cockpits of U.S. Army Apache helicopters titled "Collateral Murder" miraculously appeared on my computer screen. I knew at that moment this video would change the course of history and help bring an end to the war in Iraq. After graduation, I bought a box truck to carry all of my possessions and became a nomad. To show my gratitude for their disclosure, I decorated my truck with the WikiLeaks logo and a demand to "Release Bradley Manning." I drove the truck from the Marine Corps base in Quantico, Virginia, where Manning was confined, to the pika co-op house in Cambridge, Massachusetts and everywhere important in between. After an autumn and winter residency at the Occupy encampments in major Northeastern cities, I began covering Manning's court-martial proceedings at Ft. Meade, Maryland. For the next eighteen months I helped organize buses and vigils with activists, hitched rides with fellow journalists, and caught overnight trains to and from the pre-trial hearings. Dear friends let me crash on their floors and couches in their homes or motel rooms.

When the trial finally rolled around, so did my WikiLeaks Truck. As a credentialed journalist I did not face the same restrictions on political bumper stickers as public spectators, and I was allowed to drive on base. My credentials also afforded me the privilege of sitting on both sides of the gallery, in the jury box, and inside the remote media operations center where they projected a live feed of the trial onto a large screen.

Despite my overwhelming support for Manning, I challenged myself to document as objectively and accurately as I could muster. This was the most secretive trial in US history. Official transcripts and many of the court filings are still under seal. Yet I attended thousands of hours of proceedings and drew what I witnessed. Here I have paired those drawings with selections of unofficial transcripts published by independent journalist Alexa O'Brien and the Freedom of the Press Foundation's crowd-funded stenographers.

Shortly after the trial started, the lead prosecutor for the United States' largest information assurance case, Major Ashden Fein, boasted about his work on the trial and revealed the whereabouts of his hotel to complete strangers. Eventually this information came to my attention. Although I never sought this knowledge, nor did I confirm it to be fact, I tweeted "I don't know how they sleep at night, but I do know where" and included a link to the hotel where I had been informed the prosecution was lodging. The following day I was deemed a threat and escorted off the base by military police. Although Colonel Denise Lind allowed me to return to the courtroom, garrison commander Colonel Edward Rothstein refused to let me back on base. Unfortunately, I missed the sentencing portion of the trial. I was, however, able to piece together the last days by referencing previous sketches, friends' courtroom notes and drawings, and publicly available photographs. I wish this case had a happier ending, and I hope a future project can document that wish coming true.

Clark Stoeckley

Sunlight is said to be the best disinfectant.

Louis Brandeis, soon to be Supreme Court Justice, in 1913

The Pretrial

DECEMBER 16, 2011

FT. MEADE, MARYLAND

For the eighteen months since Manning's arrest on May 29, 2010, the government has kept the curtains closed on this high-profile trial, despite Justice Louis Brandeis's famous aphorism. Here, Private First Class Bradley Manning sits at his long-awaited hearing, guaranteed under Article 32 of the Uniform Code of Military Justice (UCMJ). The hearing will determine whether or not Manning will face a general court-martial (the most serious of military trials, and the only in which allows life in prison as a possible outcome) for allegedly releasing classified information to WikiLeaks.

FREE BRADLEY MA
JUST THE BEGINNING
United States
Fort George G Meade
Main Gate

U.S. ARMY MILITARY DISTRICT OF WASHINGTON
RULES OF HEARING
Eating and drinking are not permitted in the courtroom during open sessions, except water or other non-alcoholic beverage in an unmarked opaque container for hearing participants
Chewing gum and tobacco products are not permitted in the hearing at any time
Photographs, video, and sound recordings (except those by the detailed reporter or otherwise authorized by the investigating officer), and radio and television broadcasts shall not be made in or from the hearing during any proceedings
Cell phones, radios, pagers, iPods, Blackberries, and similar devices are not authorized in the hearing
No explosives, flammable liquids, caustic materials, or other hazardous material will be brought into the hearing without the investigating officer's prior approval
Firearms or weapons, except when used as exhibits or otherwise explicitly authorized by the investigating officer (e.g., civilian law enforcement personnel, hearing security officers), are not permitted in the hearing

POLICE
MP

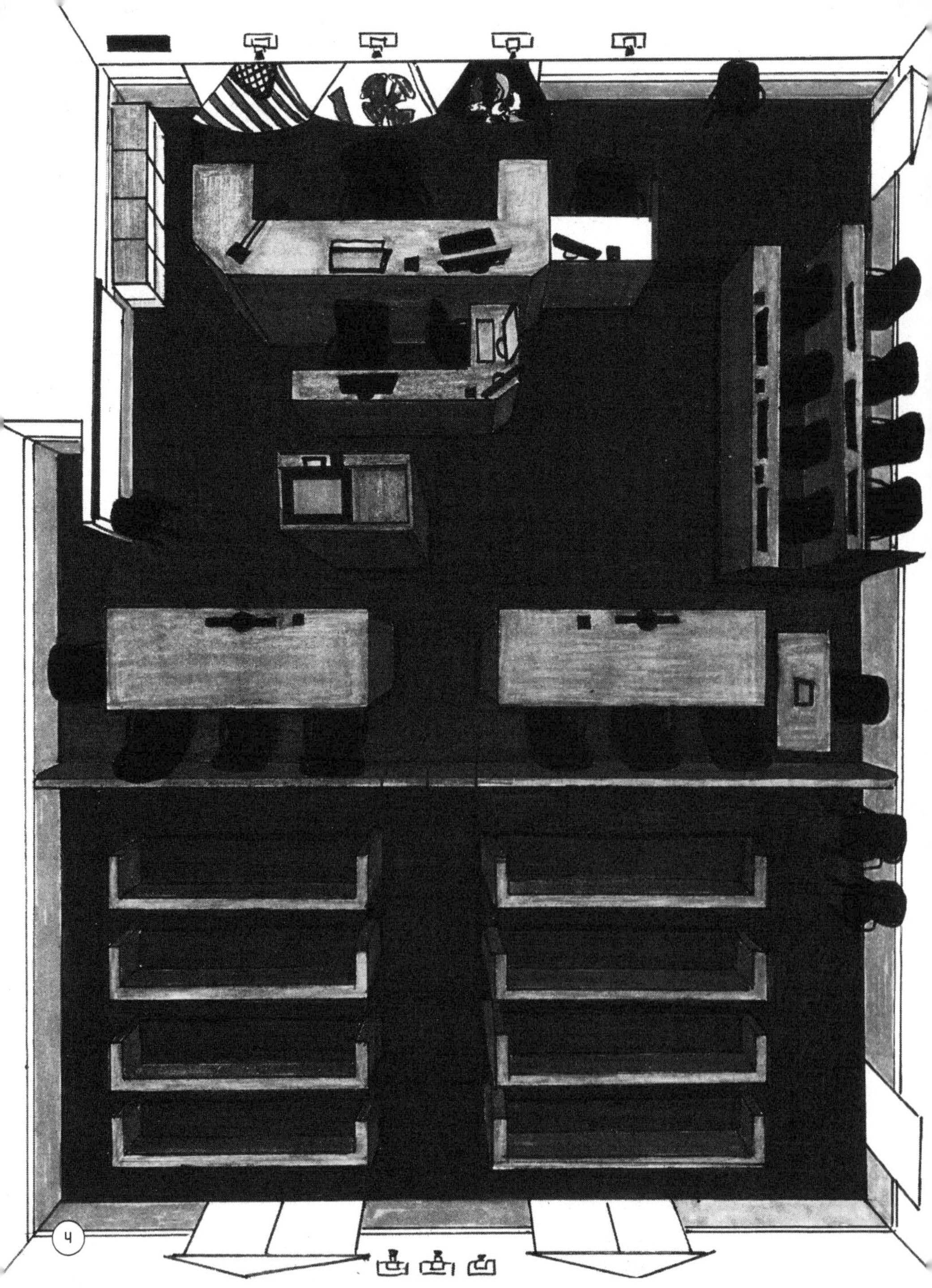
4

As investigating officer, Lieutenant Colonel Paul Almanza will look into the truth of the charges against Manning before recommending how the intelligence analyst be tried, if at all.

ALMANZA The general nature of the charges in this case are aiding the enemy, causing intelligence belonging to the United States government to be published on the Internet, transmitting national defense information to a person not entitled to receive it, stealing a record or thing of value of the United States, and failure to obey a lawful general regulation.

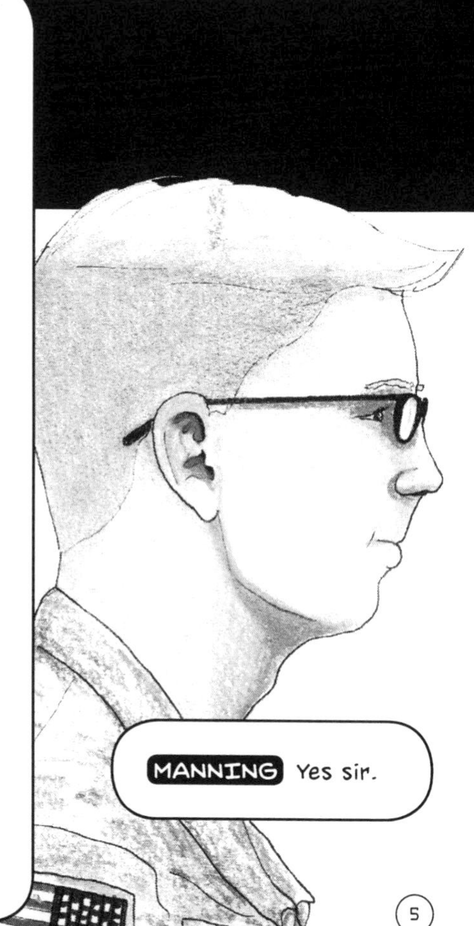
You have the right to:
1. Be present throughout the taking of evidence so long as your conduct is not disruptive.
2. Cross-examine any witnesses.
3. Present anything you might desire in your own behalf, in defense, extenuation or mitigation.
4. Have a lawyer present.
5. Have me examine available witnesses requested by you.
6. Make a statement in any form at the proper time, or to remain silent, or to refuse to make any statement regarding any offense that you are accused or suspected of, or concerning matters for which you are being investigated. Should you choose to remain silent or to make an unsworn statement, I will not hold that against you in any manner. You are advised that any statement made by you might be used as evidence against you in a trial by court-martial.
Do you understand those rights?
MANNING Yes sir.
MANNING

Leading Manning's defense team is David Coombs, a retired United States Army lieutenant colonel. He immediately disputes Almanza's supposed impartiality.

COOMBS Just the mere existence of bias is as follows: Your position as a prosecutor for the Department of Justice, coupled with an ongoing criminal grand jury investigation into WikiLeaks which the Department of Justice has not ruled out taking. The fact that you are a prosecutor at the Department of Justice independently supports your recusing yourself.

You deny it, but listening to the facts, you are not impartial. You granted every one of the government's witnesses. In their request they listed just the names, and no basis for their relevance, yet you granted them. Defense had 19 pages of relevance for each of the 38 names it requested. Of the 38, you granted only two witnesses for the defense. A "reasonable individual" would consider that biased.

Defense is filing a motion requesting that you recuse yourself. Is this the best we can do?

STATES
1775
ALMANZA
US ARMY
ALMANZA Mr. Coombs, who are you addressing?
COOMBS The public, because this is a public trial. The hallmark of our democracy is the ability of our government to be open with its public.

DECEMBER 17–21, 2011

Almanza refuses to recuse himself and all of the witnesses requested by the government testify, many over the phone from their homes or military posts. These witnesses testified in person:

Captain Casey Fulton
FULTON
Special Agent Mark Johnson
Special Agent David Shaver
Special Agent Mark Mander
Adrian Lamo
Sergeant Daniel Padgett

DECEMBER 22, 2011

COOMBS Lieutenant Colonel Almanza, you're in a unique position to give the U.S. Government something that it needs: a reality check. The government has overcharged to strong-arm a plea from my client. The U.S. Government has brought 22 charges against Manning. That means 150 years with maximum punishment, but the government wasn't satisfied with that. They also charged Manning with aiding the enemy, which carries the death penalty or life in prison without parole.
An individual who breaks a law that conscience tells him is unjust, and who willingly accepts the penalty of imprisonment in order to arouse the conscience of the community over its injustice, is in reality expressing the highest respect for the law.
In your early twenties, you believe you can change the world. You believe you can make a difference, and that's a good thing. When your president says, "Yes We Can," you actually believe that.

Major Ashden Fein, lead lawyer for the prosecution:

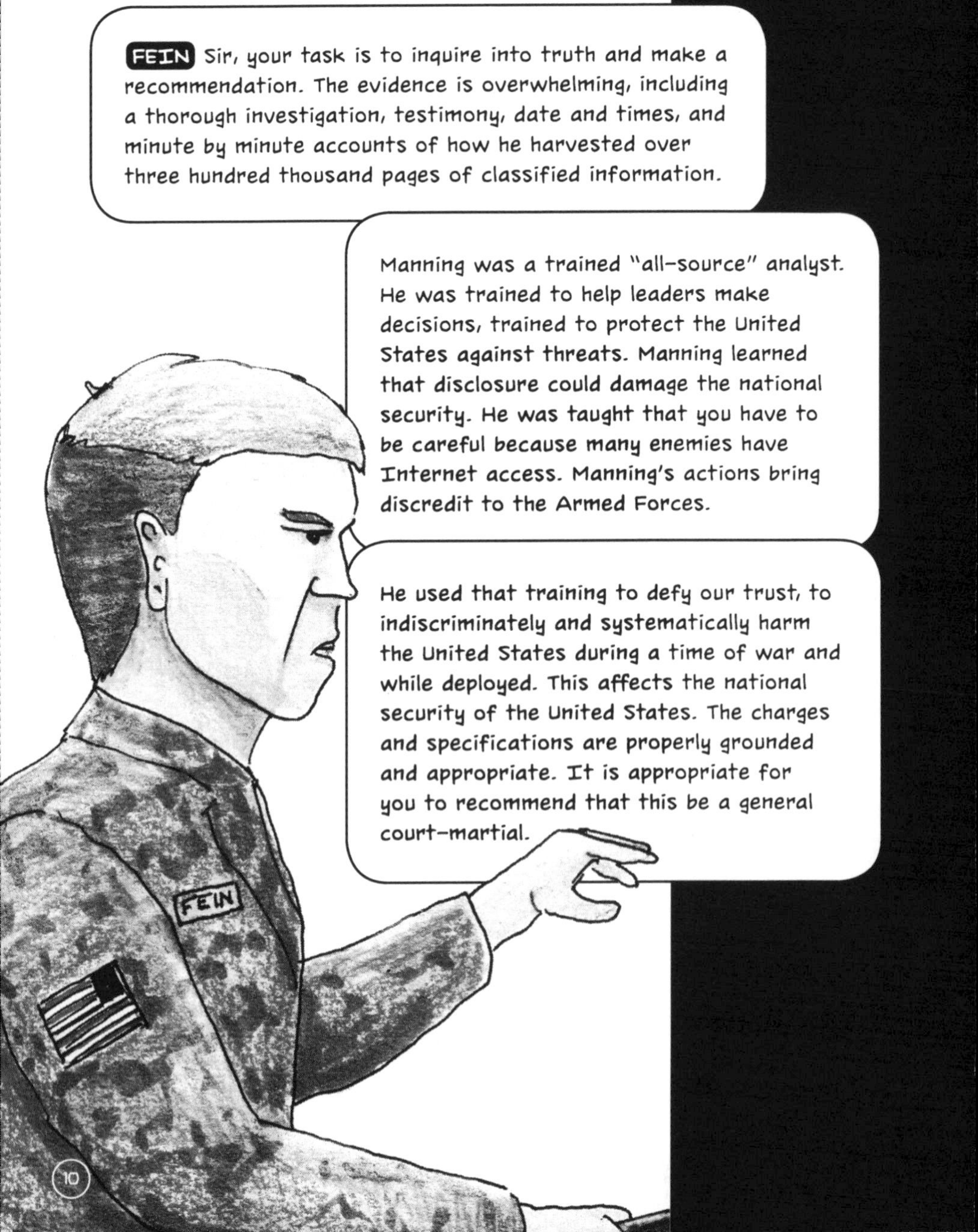

FEIN Sir, your task is to inquire into truth and make a recommendation. The evidence is overwhelming, including a thorough investigation, testimony, date and times, and minute by minute accounts of how he harvested over three hundred thousand pages of classified information.

Manning was a trained "all-source" analyst. He was trained to help leaders make decisions, trained to protect the United States against threats. Manning learned that disclosure could damage the national security. He was taught that you have to be careful because many enemies have Internet access. Manning's actions bring discredit to the Armed Forces.

He used that training to defy our trust, to indiscriminately and systematically harm the United States during a time of war and while deployed. This affects the national security of the United States. The charges and specifications are properly grounded and appropriate. It is appropriate for you to recommend that this be a general court-martial.

FEIN

FEBRUARY 23, 2012

ARRAIGNMENT

Almanza recommends a general court-martial for PFC Manning, one that will end up tarnishing the "hallmark of democracy" which Coombs invoked. The court formally arraigns Manning.

He is accused of releasing over 700,000 government documents to WikiLeaks and is charged with 22 offenses:

one count of Wrongfully Sorting Classified Information,

one count of Using an Information System Other Than Intended,

two counts of Adding Unauthorized Software,

one count of Attempting to Bypass Network Security Mechanism,

one count of Wanton Publication,

two counts of Exceeding Authorized Access under the Computer Fraud and Abuse Act,

five counts of Stealing USG Property,

eight counts of violating the Espionage Act,

and one count of Aiding the Enemy—which carries a maximum punishment of life in prison.

COOMBS What prior knowledge do you have of this case?

Military Judge Colonel Denise Lind, assigned to the trial:

LIND I knew there was a case. I knew the case involved classified information. I knew it involved a person named Manning.

COOMBS Did you view any material related to this case?

LIND No. Not that I can recall.

COOMBS What impressions, if any, do you have of this case?

LIND None.

COOMBS Any discussions?

LIND Not that I can recall.

COOMBS Formed any opinions about the case?

LIND None.

COOMBS Do you recall me teaching any classes?

LIND I think you might have. You look familiar.

The defense decides not to ask Judge Lind to recuse herself. The general court-martial now has a judge, but still needs a date. The government asks that the trial begin August 3, 2012. The defense objects.

COOMBS My client has been in pretrial confinement for 635 days. Defense has already demanded a speedy trial several times. The government is constantly citing the case's novelty, scale, and difficulty coordinating various agencies. Manning will defer his plea.

Rather than enter a plea to the government's aggressive charges and acquiesce to their protracted timeline, Manning and Coombs decide to challenge the fairness of the proceedings so far. Thus begins a series of pretrial hearings whose arguments will determine the contours of the general court-martial—the shape of arguments and the kinds of testimony allowed.

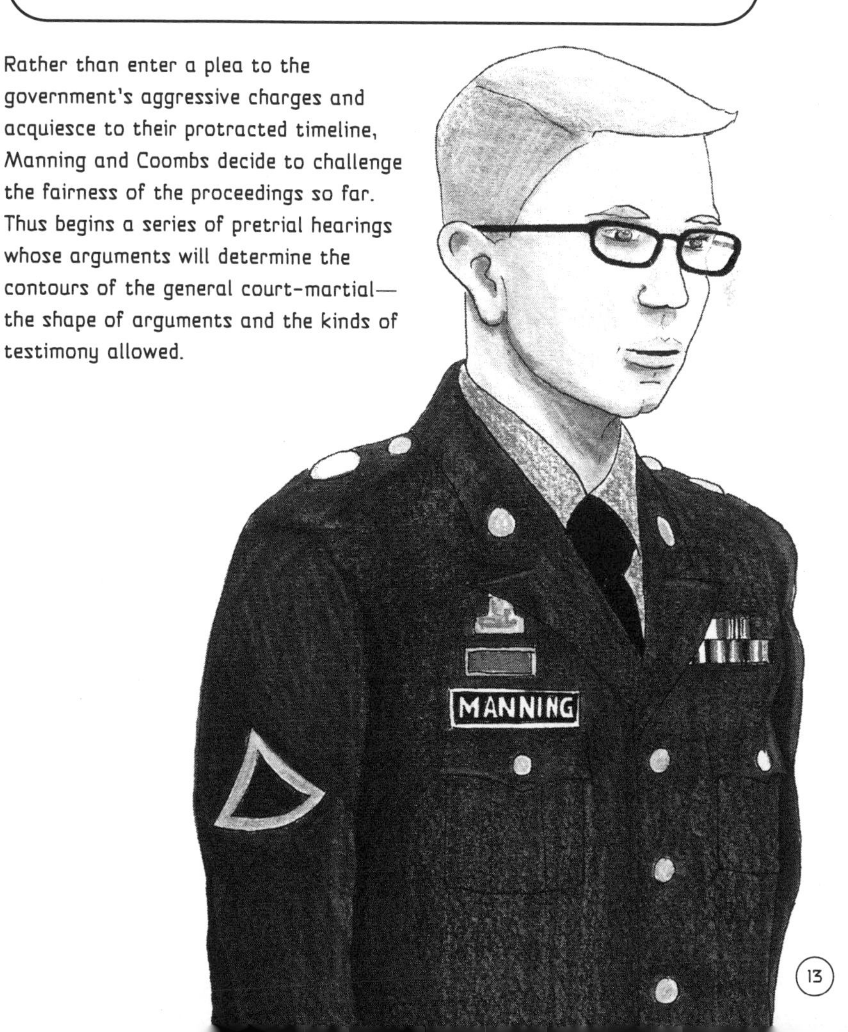
MANNING

MARCH 15, 2012

Since the arraignment, Coombs has taken important steps to render the government's case against Manning less secretive. The defense has sought certain evidence from the prosecution, including assessments of the damage caused by Manning's leaks, but to no avail. The defense asks Judge Lind to intervene and files what is called a "motion to compel discovery." If Judge Lind would grant the motion, the prosecution will have to turn over evidence it has withheld from the defense.

Despite the serious nature of the charges, the government will disclose only unclassified material. (Absurdly, this includes the still-classified documents Manning released to the public). Convinced that withholding this evidence violates Manning's right to a fair trial, a frustrated Coombs files another significant motion.

COOMBS Defense is filing a motion to permanently dismiss all charges, based on the prosecution messing up discovery of evidence so horribly.

If the motion succeeds, the government would have to charge and arraign Manning anew.

Later that same afternoon, Coombs argues for another motion, this one to "compel deposition." Coombs wants to have U.S. Government officials (called "Original Classification Authorities") responsible for determining that the charged releases needed protection give evidence on the alleged harm of Manning's releases – and in doing so possibly open line of argument against the charge that Manning aided the enemy.

COOMBS Defense is in the position of not being able to prepare for the trial. We requested Original Classification Authorities as essential witnesses for the Article 32 hearing. The investigating officer improperly denied them. They were essential witnesses, because for over a year trial was delayed on getting determinations on how to classify the released information. We as defense should have access to those. If these authorities can articulate why a certain release would cause damage, then defense would like to cross-examine them, and should have already been able to do so, rather than waiting for the trial to begin.

The government impeded our access to these authorities. If they are vital for government's case, then they are vital to the defense's case. We asked government, "Please give us contact info for civilian Original Classification Authorities." Government said, "No." I said, "Can you please explain your response?" "Sure" they said. We waited one month, but heard nothing.

LIND The investigating officer, Lt. Col. Almanza, properly balanced the significance of each witness' testimony against the difficulty, expense, and effect on military operations of obtaining his or her presence in the investigation. The investigating officer properly considered the Original Classification Authority affidavits instead. The government has not impeded defense access to the Original Classification Authorities. There is no evidence that any of the witnesses will be unavailable for trial should they be deemed relevant and necessary. There is good cause to deny the request for depositions for all of the witnesses.

Lind schedules the next proceedings for April 24 to 26. The motion to dismiss all charges remains the subject of a future hearing. At this point Manning can either remain in pretrial confinement as Coombs continues to file motions that might strengthen his defense, or proceed to trial without the best possible case

APRIL 24, 2012

The government has allegedly seen sworn testimony from a federal grand jury investigation into WikiLeaks. Coombs argues for a motion to compel the discovery of testimony from the investigation.

COOMBS In the military, we pride ourselves on open discovery. You don't play "hide the ball" like the government's been doing. You get discovery out there and you have a trial on the facts. The prosecution is engaged in revisionist history. If they understood their obligations, they already would have provided us this information, and they're not able to do that today.

It cannot be that the prosecution can interact with other agencies and then claim it has no control over documents. The government should not be able to stash away documents within other agencies.

APRIL 25, 2012

In a setback for the defense, Lind denies both the motion to dismiss all charges and the motion to compel discovery of WikiLeaks grand jury proceedings.

ORIGINAL

LIND Defense moves the court to compel the government to produce the entire grand jury proceedings in relation to Manning or WikiLeaks as material to the preparation of the defense.

The government opposes on the grounds that FBI files are classified, Department of Justice files relating to the accused and WikiLeaks are law enforcement – sensitive and contain grand jury information, and that the prosecution has no authority to produce any FBI or Department of Justice files that have not already been produced to the defense. There have been one or more grand jury investigations involving WikiLeaks.

LIND The government has access to the FBI investigation files and the grand jury proceedings for the purpose of reviewing them for favorable information material to the defendant's guilt or punishment that must be disclosed to the defense. Grand jury proceedings are not discoverable. Grand jury proceedings are secret. Federal courts require parties seeking access to grand jury transcripts to show a particularized need and that the material they seek is necessary to avoid a possible injustice, that the need for disclosure is greater than the need for continued secrecy.
The defense has not demonstrated a basis for the relevance and necessity of these files, much less the particularized need required to access grand jury transcripts. The defense motion to compel production of the entire grand jury investigation involving the accused and WikiLeaks is denied.

TOOMAN In particular the word "injury" is vague. It is unclear what type of injury is required. Is it physical injury? Is it embarrassment? Is it monetary injury? That is unclear. What is also unclear is the extent of the injury that is required. Is it minimal injury—just the scantest little thing—or does it have to be some grave injury? National security is not a phrase that is meant to protect the government from things that are embarrassing.
US
US
TOOMAN

JUNE 7, 2012

Judge Lind denies this motion, citing 1988's *The U.S. v. Morrison*—the case of a Navy analyst who used top-secret clearance to send photographs of a Soviet battleship under construction to a small magazine reporting on international naval operations where he worked on the side. One photograph ended up in the *Washington Post*. That judge gave his opinion:

And that term, the term national defense, includes all matters that directly or may reasonably be connected with the defense of the United States against any of its enemies. It refers to the military and naval establishments and the related activities of national preparedness. To prove that the documents or the photographs relate to national defense there are two things that the government must prove. First, it must prove that the disclosure of the photographs would be potentially damaging to the United States or might be useful to an enemy of the United States. Secondly, the government must prove that the documents or the photographs are closely held in that they have not been made public and are not available to the general public.

Lind hews close to this precedent as *The US v. PFC Bradley Manning* continues to wrestle with concepts of security and secrecy.

JUNE 8, 2012

Despite the government's assurances to the contrary, the defense obtains two memos admitting nine months of inactivity on their legal obligation to provide "Brady" material—that which is material to the guilt or innocence of a defendant.

Coombs submits the memos alongside a motion to compel discovery of damage assessments from various government agencies. In the courtroom, testimony from State Department witnesses reveals new discoverable material of the sort Coombs implies the government is withholding.

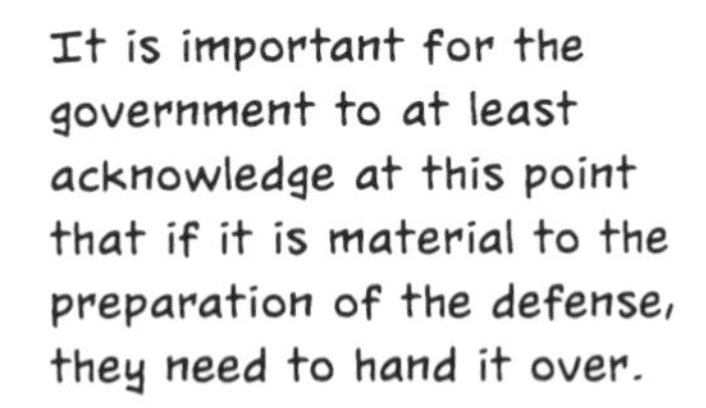

COOMBS We said if there are documents that are material to the preparation of the defense in the possession of these agencies, we want them. The government has consistently responded, "You haven't given us a basis to hand them over." If you look at it, and you say to yourself, "I would really like to have this if I were a defense counsel," that should tip you off and you should hand it over.
It is important for the government to at least acknowledge at this point that if it is material to the preparation of the defense, they need to hand it over.

The memos seem to put the prosecution on its heels, and Judge Lind grants their request to delay her ruling until the next hearing, on June 25.

JUNE 25, 2012

COOMBS We are two years in. Why is the government still in the process of reviewing and providing these documents to the defense? We have a pattern of issues that should alarm the court. The government is trying to define its way out of discovery. This type of discovery battle is almost unheard of in military court.

FEIN The defense is trying to create additional obligations. The prosecution never claimed that we have completed our search, but that we are completing our search, which is what we've been doing since then and will continue to do.

COOMBS We're asking the court to ensure for itself, and anyone watching this case, that the prosecution is complying with its discovery obligations. They say it'll be done soon, but what have they been doing for the last two years? We have too many problems to take them at their word. It doesn't appear that they know what they're doing.

Finally, Judge Lind grants the defense a victory—small, but appreciable.

LIND The law requires the government to disclose information obviously relevant and helpful to the preparation of the defense. The government in reviewing files will provide the defense any information beyond the investigation, damage, and mitigation measures that are obviously relevant and helpful to the defense.

This is a complex case involving multiple government agencies and entities. The court makes no findings of lack of due diligence by the government. Both parties will have an opportunity to litigate the due diligence of the government in providing discovery during the speedy trial motion.

The government will identify what classified filings have not been identified to the defense. The defense motion for due diligence filing is granted in part.

JULY 16–19, 2012

With the defense expecting to receive damage assessments and more after Judge Lind's ruling, the government submits a motion to preclude the defense from discussing during the trial the harm Manning's releases caused (or did not cause). But the defense finds the issue relevant to Manning's state of mind at the time he released the documents—a crucial aspect for their argument that the soldier acted with good intentions, not to aid the enemy.

FEIN All of that testimony should be impeached if they are using opinion about harm. If it "could" cause harm it is confidential and secret.

So again, defense would be able to cross-examine, just not as to whether damage to national security occurred. All specifications in the charges are to hold the accused accountable for either theft or disclosure and are complete at offense or transmission. If the court adopts the defense's argument, the offense hasn't occurred until the damage is known.

The government convinces Judge Lind that harm is irrelevant to the charges Manning faces. What matters, the prosecution and Judge Lind agree, was the possibility of harm at the time Manning released the documents.

NOVEMBER 7, 2012

Hearings begin for the defense's motion that the court has violated Manning's right to a speedy trial. The government calls classification expert Bert Haggett and the Special Court-Martial Convening Authority overseeing this pretrial, Colonel Carl Coffman, to justify its delays. On cross-examination, the defense demonstrates the overwhelming duration of the proceedings when it presses Haggett to provide specific dates for his work on the case.

HURLEY When were you first contacted? Do you recall a deadline? How long did the Original Classification Authority take?
HAGGETT I don't recall.
NOVEMBER 8, 2012
COOMBS Have you ever considered denying the prosecution's request for delays?
COFFMAN No.
COFFMAN

NOVEMBER 27, 2012

It has been more than two years since Manning's arrest, and the hearings finally turn to the length and conditions of the whistle-blower's pretrial confinement. The military first placed Manning in confinement at Camp Arifjan, Kuwait, on May 27, 2010 before moving him to Quantico, VA about one month later. There, the military designated him a "maximum custody" prisoner and put him on "Prevention of Injury" and "Suicide Risk" statuses.

Retired Colonel Daniel Choike, former Quantico Brig Commander:

CHOIKE There were claims he was in solitary. He was not. Punitive segregation was not utilized. Quantico is not about long term—it's about individual short term, but not long term, confinement.

And yet Manning spent 258 days at Quantico—many more than the recommended 90 days—in conditions the defense maintain unlawful pretrial punishment, while the Sanity Board delayed determining whether Manning was

NOVEMBER 28, 2012

Navy Captain Dr. William Hocter, the psychiatrist that treated Manning:

HOCTER Even at Guantanamo Bay my recommendations were implemented much faster than at Quantico. He spent an unprecedented amount of time under precautions. It would often take up to two weeks for the staff to implement recommendations to change a prisoner's status, in contrast with the few days it would take elsewhere.

HOCTER

Security Battalion Commander at Quantico Marine Colonel Robert Oltman:

OLTMAN The guidance that Hocter gave was wrong. I was going to be very cautious of the opinions that he gave.

Colonel Dr. Rick Malone, another psychiatrist who treated Manning for nearly four months at Quantico:

MALONE Several weeks after he arrived at Quantico, he was taken off his anti-anxiety medications—celexa and clonazepam—because he was symptom-free, in complete remission, and posed no harm to himself or others. But the way he was being held was detrimental to his physical and mental health. His custody status was a stressor.

Navy psychiatrist Captain Dr. Kevin Moore also testifies that Manning's isolation conditions were more severe than that of death row inmates.

NOVEMBER 29, 2012

In much anticipated testimony, Manning himself takes the stand as a witness for the defense:

MANNING At Camp Arifjan, my nights were my days, and my days were my nights, so it all blended together after a couple days. My phone privileges were removed shortly after my first three phone calls. I don't know why.

I was in a pretty stressful situation. They don't allow news there. They don't have any TV. They didn't allow radio. I started to really deteriorate in terms of my awareness of my surroundings and what was going on. I was more insular—anxious all the time about not knowing anything.

I usually have pretty solid knowledge of what's going on—like in terms of my job, or my family, or current events that are going on. I am usually grounded pretty firmly in those things, in how I connect to the rest of the world. After having those cut off, I just started to not really get anything.

I just started living inside the limited surroundings that I had. My world just shrunk to just that cage.

I remember thinking I am going to die. I am stuck here in this cage, and I don't know what is going to happen. I just pretty much had given up on a lot of things. I didn't know what time of day it was or anything else. I didn't think I was going to set foot on American soil for a long time.
MANNING

COOMBS This cell that we see in white tape on the courtroom floor—how many hours each day would you be in this cell at Quantico?

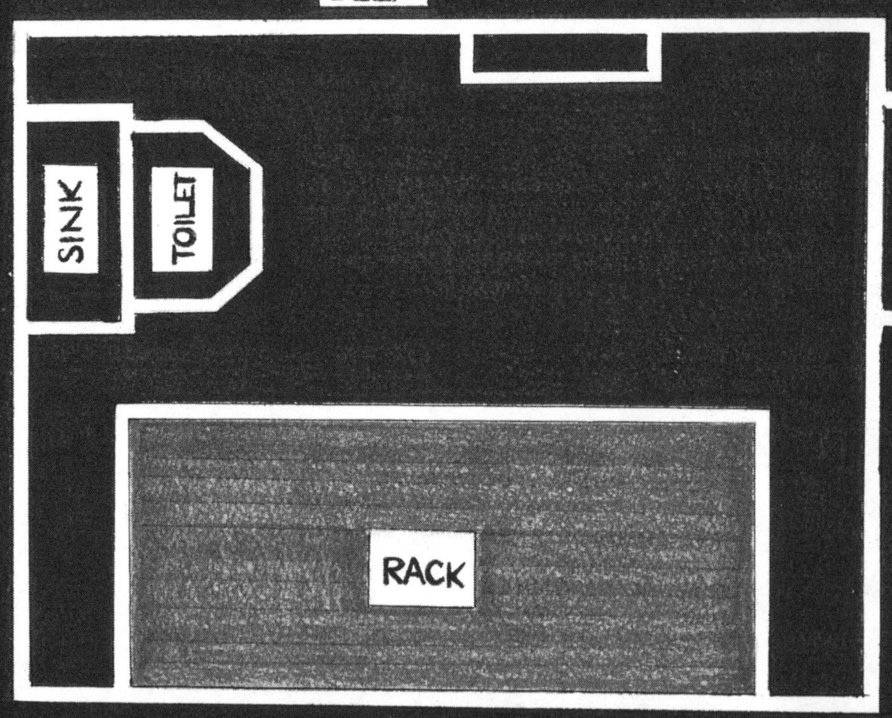
8 FEET DEEP
6 FEET WIDE
SINK
TOILET
RACK

MANNING Depending on what the schedule of calls was for that day, and visitation to other areas, like a legal visit or a counselor visit outside of my cell. It was between 21 and 23 hours—sometimes even over 23—as much as 23 and a half hours a day. I would normally sit and try to keep myself occupied. I would usually sit on the rack. Sometimes they would allow me to have my legs up on the rack, in an Indian-style position, but sometimes that was not authorized.

MANNING It is abrasive on skin. It became a routine thing that I got a bit of a rash, but there was nothing that I could really do for it.

COOMBS Did you need any assistance getting out of the suicide smock?
RACK

MANNING I did. I was still taking some sleep medication at the time. The smock is strong so I couldn't get out of it on my own.

MANNING There was no reasonable way of accessing natural light. I ate every meal inside of the cell. I did not have glasses. I cannot see without my glasses. The entire day I sat upright. I was technically allowed to speak to other detainees, but the cells on either side of me were empty, and talking to someone farther away would have violated the "conversational tone" rules. I never had sheets or blankets. If I needed toilet paper, then I would stand up to the front of the door and announce to the observation room "request permission to use toilet paper." Sometimes they say they would get it, and then they didn't.

COOMBS Were you allowed to exercise in your cell?

MANNING No. There wasn't a lot to do. I would just try to move around as much as I could even if it was just minor movements every so often. That way I can keep the blood flowing and stay awake.

For 'sunshine call', the 20 minute period, I would be taken outside in full restraints. They would have always at least one guard holding me, and we would walk usually in circles or in figure 8's. There was electronic exercise equipment. I was told that most of it didn't work. They didn't want me to touch anything electronic, whatsoever. They had treadmills and weight lifting equipment, but if it plugged into something or had any computer, they didn't allow me to touch it. They were concerned about that.

MANNING I started asking Captain Hocter why he wasn't recommending me to come off of Prevention of Injury status. He kept saying that he was, but then Gunnery Sergeant Blenis, my counselor, kept on saying it was the docs that were recommending that status.

I started to notice a discrepancy in the information that I was receiving, and that's when I became concerned. I would talk to Hocter about at least once a week as well as Master Sergeant Blenis once a week. I was always asking Blenis, "How am I doing?" He would usually give me an "A" rating. I kept asking Hocter, "Why are you recommending me to stay on POI?" and he'd be like, "I'm not." I just wanted to get off of this restrictive status, and at least be allowed to sleep with sheets and blanket, have soap in my cell – things like that. Those were high priorities in my mind.

I wasn't sure who was telling the truth. I was in a cell all day, so my mind wandered. I was mentally going back into that lonely, dark, black hole. The most entertaining thing in there was the mirror. You can interact with yourself. I spent quite a lot of time at the mirror. Just sheer, complete, out-of-my-mind boredom.

QUANTICO

CROSSROADS OF THE MARINE CORPS

FREE BRAD MANNING

The defense alleges the brig staff punished Manning for the unwanted attention of a January 17, 2011 rally in his support.

COOMBS Now I am going to ask you a few questions about an incident on 18 January 2011. When you were taken out of your cell for recreation call, what, if anything, happened that caused you to be concerned?

MANNING They put on the leg irons slightly tighter than normal. I remember asking them if they were irritated or if I was doing something wrong. They don't respond. We go to the recreation area. They tell me to face left, and I face left. But I have another person tell me to face right. I start to panic a little bit, because I don't know what's about to happen. I never had the guards act like that before. Everything you do is wrong no matter what, because you're given conflicting orders.

I ask them to stop, but they continue at it and then I begin to fall. One guard comes at me and I thought I was going to be attacked. My instant reaction was to get away. I was not feeling very—my judgment was not perfect at that time. So, you know, I just get away. I said, "Please stop," you know, "I am trying to cooperate as much as I can." I think at that point I got emotional. They said, "We're gonna get somebody here to talk to you." I felt like I was being roughed around a little bit.

MANNING He stopped right outside my cell. So I'm standing at attention, and I remember him saying something to the effect of "Why are you violating my trust? I've allowed you this recreation call, so why are you causing trouble?
COOMBS So he was asking you questions about what happened?
MANNING No, no, no. He was saying—he didn't ask questions until later. But, I was told to relax at some point and then he started asking me questions.
COOMBS When you started pushing back—"Hey I don't feel I need to be in POI, I don't understand why I am in POI"—how did Chief Averhart respond?
MANNING He was furious. I've only seen an officer this angry twice in my life. He was yelling at me at this point. I went back to attention and just listened. Then he left and told the guards, "Special move: Suicide Risk."
I lost my demeanor at that point. You know, I am trying to keep from losing my recreation call, and I'm being put on—I am going back to square one. I almost punched the wall.

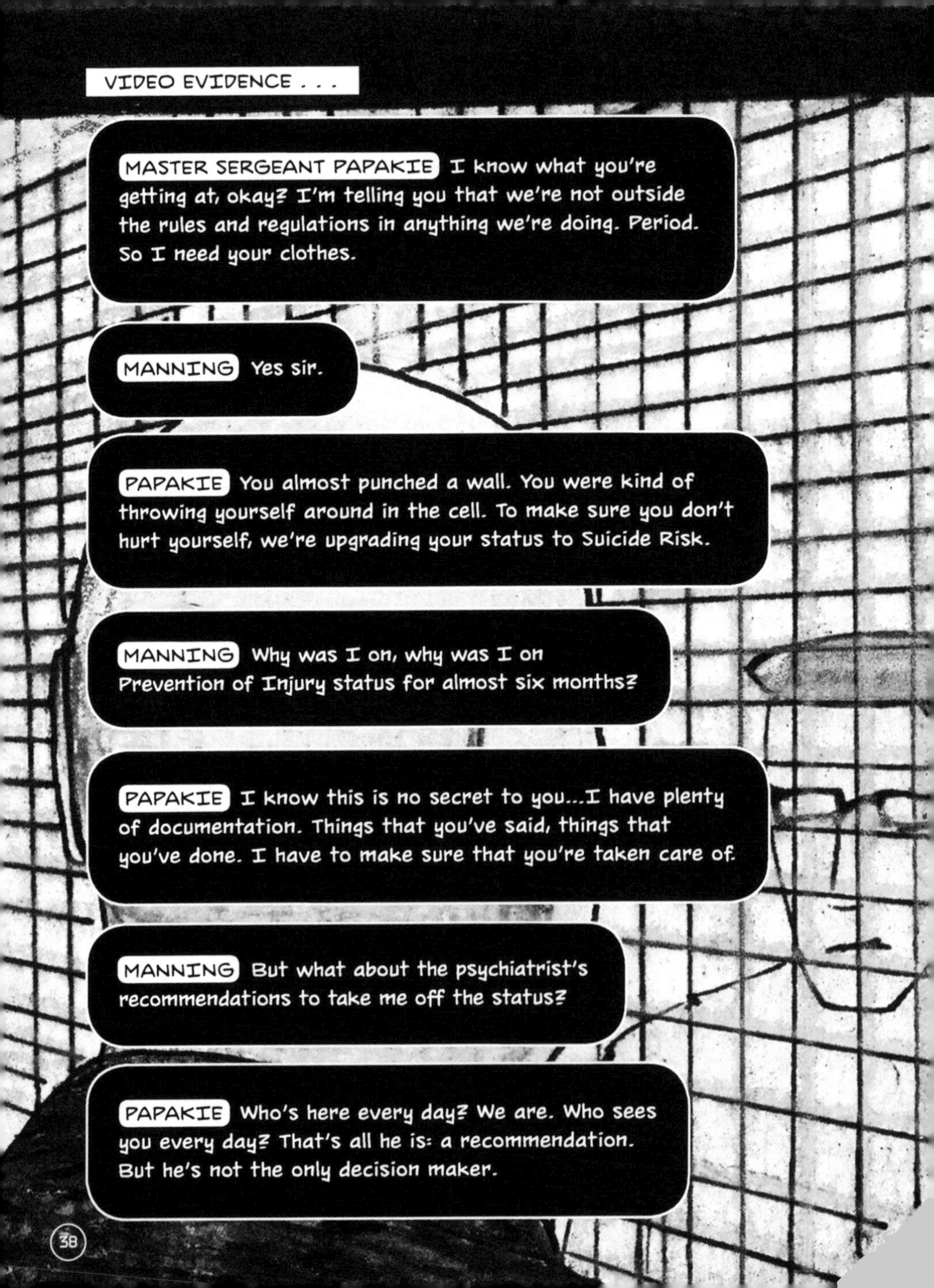

VIDEO EVIDENCE . . .

MASTER SERGEANT PAPAKIE I know what you're getting at, okay? I'm telling you that we're not outside the rules and regulations in anything we're doing. Period. So I need your clothes.

MANNING Yes sir.

PAPAKIE You almost punched a wall. You were kind of throwing yourself around in the cell. To make sure you don't hurt yourself, we're upgrading your status to Suicide Risk.

MANNING Why was I on, why was I on Prevention of Injury status for almost six months?

PAPAKIE I know this is no secret to you...I have plenty of documentation. Things that you've said, things that you've done. I have to make sure that you're taken care of.

MANNING But what about the psychiatrist's recommendations to take me off the status?

PAPAKIE Who's here every day? We are. Who sees you every day? That's all he is: a recommendation. But he's not the only decision maker.

MANNING I was getting anxious because they were getting anxious. It seemed to me that they were looking for something wrong. I'm getting increasingly frustrated because I'm trying to do everything I can not to be a concern, therefore I appear as though I'm causing more concern. When will I be taken off of Prevention of Injury status? What's being used to justify the precautions? I'm constantly trying to figure it out.

GUNNERY SERGEANT BLENIS As a facility, we have to always err on the side of caution, okay? Not just caution, but over-caution. Especially when we're talking about suicide, okay? Nobody's saying you're going to kill yourself, all right? It's not a punitive thing. I can tell you that since you have been here I wish I had a hundred Mannings

MANNING That's why I don't understand the continuation of the restrictions beyond the time recommended by you and the psychiatrist. I've got my own forensic psychiatrist that's now saying that Prevention of Injury status is actually doing psychiatric harm.

COOMBS How many days, from your memory, were you on Suicide Risk, before you were put back on POI?

MANNING It was less than a week if I recall correctly.

MANNING On March 2, about month and a half later, Papakie came by and did a check. This was unusual: he stopped by the cell and he told me to relax. I decided that it's been a bit of time since I raised this, and he seemed to be in a good mood, so I started to talk. I just wanted to convey the fact that I'd been on the status for a long time, and I am not doing anything to harm myself.
I told him "I'm not throwing myself against the walls or, you know, trying to stick my head into the toilet and drown." I said, "If I really wanted to hurt myself wouldn't I just use the things that are here now, the underwear, the flip-flops? When does it stop? Does it stop with removing walls?"
I actually thought that maybe my point had gotten across, because he was nodding. A couple hours later the guards came with different handling instructions for the night. They removed my underwear, and they took my flip-flops. I slept with my Prevention of Injury blankets and mattress. They took my glasses, t-shirt, and socks, too.
MANNING

MANNING In the morning they announced, "Reveille Reveille Reveille" as they do every morning at zero-five. I grabbed the Prevention of Injury blanket and stood at parade rest. They announced, "Stand by for count." I couldn't see because my glasses were taken away. The guard from the observation booth opened the door a crack and asked, "Is that how you stand at parade rest, detainee Manning?" He said, "You know what to do," or something like that, but I knew it was an indirect command. I placed my blanket back on the mattress, and stood at parade rest. I had no socks, no underwear, nothing.

COOMBS While you are standing there naked at parade rest, did anyone direct you at that point, "Private Manning, cover yourself with the blanket"?

MANNING No. I stood at attention for a minute and a half to conduct count, and then I was standing at parade rest for another three or four minutes until they did the "All clear."

DECEMBER 1, 2012

With the Manning's testimony ringing in their ears, the prosecution must show a legitimate government interest to justify the conditions of Manning's pretrial confinement, especially his extended time on Prevention of Injury status.

Gunnery Sergeant William Fuller explains what Quantico's Classification and Assignment Board considered when determining Manning's confinement status each week. He tesified that Manning's distant and withdrawn behavior encouraged their weekly recommendations to keep him on POI status. Fuller also conceded that poor family relationships and the severity of his charges—influences beyond Manning's control—also factored into the board's decisions.

FULLER A lot of times I heard from officers that Manning didn't communicate as much later on in his confinement as he did in the beginning.

The government calls Quantico guards to testify.

STAFF SERGEANT RYAN JORDAN When he was first brought into confinement I believe he gave an alias of Breanna Elizabeth Manning.

COOMBS If a detainee has a gender identity disorder, would that be a factor to put a detainee in Prevention of Injury?

JORDAN Depends on how that individual is affected. I considered it in my decision to keep Manning on Prevention of Injury but it didn't weigh heavy.

JORDAN
WITNESS

DECEMBER 2, 2012

MASTER SERGEANT CRAIG BLENIS Week to week he st
to speak more. After seven to eight weeks, he stopped talk
That went on for three or four weeks. Then he started spe
me again but that was a brief two weeks. I've got a perso
communicating with me that's sitting in his cell, not doing a

If someone tells me they're going
to shoot themselves in the face,
I'm not going to give them a gun.

DECEMBER 5, 2012

Defense cross-examines Master Sergeant Brian Papakie:

PAPAKIE Answering a question on his intake forms about suicide, he wrote, "Always planning, never acting." For someone to say something like that, I can't just brush that off.

Coombs has Papakie read instructions he gave the guards:

PAPAKIE "Make sure he is not standing at attention naked for evening count right before taps. You should be taking his panties right before he lays down."

COOMBS Do Marines refer to male underwear as panties?

PAPAKIE I have on multiple occasions. Like as in, "Don't get my panties in a bunch." It is just a choice of words, but I agree it is a poor choice.

Coombs cross-examines Chief Warrant Officer 5 Abel Galaviz, Head of Marine Corrections, and asks for an opinion on the fact that Master Sergeant Blenis, as Manning's counselor, wrote weekly recommendations to keep Manning on POI before then serving as a member of the board that reviewed Manning's status.

COOMBS Do you see a problem?

GALAVIZ The individual making the recommendations should not also be serving as a board member. He already has his opinion and it's his position to make recommendations to others encouraging their support. For him to serve as a board member, I don't think he is able to vote against his recommendation.

WITNESS

DECEMBER 6, 2012

Chief Warrant Officer 4 Averhart, Brig Officer In Charge (OIC), ordered commanding officers to keep Manning on Prevention of Injury Status until the Sanity Board finished its review.

AVERHART Other prisoners in Quantico were very patriotic. They knew why Manning was there. They knew the allegations against him. I was aware of the media attention in the papers and television and was concerned that anything could happen.

Dr. Hocter was just going through the motions. Blenis's recommendations meant a lot to me because he was the individual who spent more time with Manning.

Coombs confronts Averhart with an email from M. Sgt. Blenis containing a facetious draft for an upcoming report:

On December 13 2010, a package from Amazon.com was delivered to the Brig by a construction worker who works nearby. There was no previous request for a package submitted by Manning and there was no previous approval for a package. When asked about any potential packages that may be coming, Manning stated that he was not aware of any but thought that family members may be sending something due to his upcoming birthday. The package is being rejected and returned to sender due to the manner in which it was received and also because there was no prior request or knowledge of the package, and there was no pre-approval given, and *we felt like being dicks.*

AVERHART It was inappropriate and tasteless and shouldn't have been made. It was not professional.

DECEMBER 7, 2012

Chief Warrant Officer 2 Denise Barnes, on the stand here, replaced Averhart in January 2011. She authorized Papakie to take his underwear and flip-flops. Barnes was ultimately responsible for Manning's classification until he transferred to Ft. Leavenworth in April 2011.

BARNES We all know you don't have to have a mental health issue to want to kill yourself. If somebody really wants to commit suicide, they're not going to tell us that. The main issue is just coming out directly and saying "I do not want to harm myself."

DECEMBER 10, 2012

BARNES I am looking at someone who is in the friggin' brig, so that alone will add to his stress and depression especially once the pace of the legal proceedings pick up. It will only get worse once the true weight of his legal situation and future hits him.

I don't take this crap lightly. It's not professional. We know that. What he said about the flip-flops and underwear was one small comment, but I don't want something to friggin' explode and hurt Manning and someone in the staff. I friggin' take it personal when people say I have something against Manning or any other detainee. I'm a wife. I'm a mother. I take my position very seriously. I apologize if I'm getting heated, but at the end of the day, I have someone to answer to. I don't take it personally against any detainee.

DECEMBER 11, 2012

COOMBS DEFENDS MANNING'S BEHAVIOR

LT. GEN. FLYNN
COL. CHOIKE
COL. OLTMAN
CW4 AVERHART
CW2 BARNES
MSGT. PAPAKIE
MSGT. BLENIS
MDW SJA SHOP
COL. COFFMAN
ARMY OTJAG

COOMBS It is clear Manning does the only sane thing and that's to stop communicating with these people because when he says anything it's used against him. Communication is a two-way street. Did they go and tell him certain behavior was of concern to them? Never.

The system fed off itself. At best there was an incestuous relationship with everybody at the brig and in the Marine Corps chain of command. The safest position for them was the status quo. They might even have had good intentions. The problem was their intentions were not required.

COOMBS They watched this young man 24/7, but they can only point to a small handful of behaviors—sword fighting with imaginary characters, dancing, or playing peek-a-boo with the mirror. Manning was moved around in full shackles in the facility. Hocter, Malone, and Jordan each testified Manning had been held in conditions they had only previously seen imposed on death row detainees. He was held on Prevention Of Injury for the majority of his confinement, which was extraordinary since it is supposed to be a temporary status.

COOMBS What happened when Manning was moved to Leavenworth is the best evidence Manning did not need to be in onerous conditions to ensure his presence at a trial. He has been allowed recreation call. He has been able to move outside his cell freely, without chains. He has been allowed personal items in his cell. And he has not tried to harm himself. There, the commanding officers listen to their doctors.

The defense requests the dismissal of all charges. If the court does not want to give this relief, which it can give, the court should issue a ten-days-to-one credit for days when Manning was unlawfully punished while he was there, in confinement, for over two hundred days.

MAJ. ASHDEN FEIN RESPONDS

FEIN The United States government argues Quantico staff had one interest: to protect Manning from harming himself and others while ensuring he was present for future proceedings. The treatment was not so excessive as to constitute punishment, considering factors like the potential length of sentence, poor family relationships and home conditions, low tolerance of frustration and disruptive behavior. He could have been on suicide risk all the time.

Communication was not ideal, but Manning never went without mental health care. Manning as a detainee did not have the authority to second-guess the decisions of the brig officers. Manning was not like the other detainees and the officers did their best to try and figure him out so they could take care of him properly.

US
US
FEIN

COLONEL DENISE LIND, MILITARY JUDGE, READS HER RULING

LIND The government concedes that maintaining the accused on suicide risk after mental health provider determined he was no longer a suicide risk constitutes unlawful pretrial punishment. The court agrees. The accused will receive one day of confinement credit starting the day after Captain Hocter recommended the accused be removed from suicide risk.

The accused was not, however, held in solitary confinement. He had daily human contact. The brig staff of Quantico chain of command had no intent to punish the accused. Dismissal of charges is not an appropriate remedy for any violations in this case.

STATES ARMY
1775

LIND At some point, continuing Prevention of Injury status over the recommendation of a mental health professional becomes excessive in relation to the legitimate government interest of keeping the accused from harming himself, even if brig officials disagree with the diagnosis of the mental health professional. This decision is a very close call.
Testimony and Marine Corps Brig Quantico policy indicate that one hour of exercise is the standard for all prisoners unless limited because of prisoner behavior and staff resource constraints. The court grants ten days of sentence credit.
Any comments that may be perceived as derogatory statements made about the accused in e-mails between the brig staff were not communicated to the accused or any other prisoner, and were not humiliating to the accused. No sentencing credit is warranted.
The accused has been granted with 112 days of sentence credit for pretrial punishments.

JANUARY 9, 2013

THE GOVERNMENT'S DISTURBING JURISPRUDENCE REVEALED

COOMBS There's been no case in the entire history of military jurisprudence that involved sending information to a legitimate journalistic organization which resulted in an aiding-the-enemy prosecution. Such a determination ignores the elephant in the room: over-classification. Why is it relevant how WikiLeaks was viewed? What's the difference between WikiLeaks and the *New York Times*? There's no difference. The government seems to think there is one.
truth
truth
MANNING
LIND If we substituted the *New York Times* for WikiLeaks, would the government charge Bradley Manning in the same way that you have?

OVERGAARD Yes.

SPEEDY TRIAL HEARINGS CAN RESUME

Major Fein takes the podium to argue that the government has not also violated Manning's right to a speedy trial.

FEIN We were never in a waiting posture that would have delayed the trial and violated Manning's rights. Crimes are typically complete and the effects of the crime are known. But in this case we didn't know the total amount of information or evidence because there was still information Manning compromised that could have been released. There has been no military justice case that required the amount of coordination inside the defense Department and outside of the department than this one.
TIMELINE

Seemingly tired of the prosecution's verbal contortions, Coombs's insists that an examination of email evidence will show the government's unreasonable delays.

COOMBS If you don't want to take the spin from the government or the defense, e-mails are objective, so look at those.

FEBRUARY 26, 2013

JUDGE LIND RULES . . .

LIND This is a complex case involving voluminous classified information in the custody of multiple government agencies having national security concerns. To date, the government has produced 526,366 pages of discovery with 437,000 pages of classified discovery. The reasons for the delay justify the length of the delay.

The test isn't whether the government could have acted with greater speed. It is whether the government acted with reasonable diligence. In this case, it did.

The Motion to Dismiss For Lack of a Speedy Trial under Sixth Amendment is denied.

FEBRUARY 28, 2013

Back in November, shortly before testifying about conditions at Quantico, Manning announced his significant decision to plea "by exceptions and substitutions" and elected to be tried by a judge alone instead of a panel of soldiers. If Judge Lind finds his plea "provident," then he can no longer be found entirely not guilty. Coombs explained their decision on his blog:

> To clarify, PFC Manning is not pleading guilty to the specifications as charged by the government. Rather, PFC Manning is attempting to accept responsibility for offenses that are encapsulated within, or are a subset of, the charged offenses. The court will consider whether this is a permissible plea. Further, the government does not need to agree to PFC Manning's plea . . . the government may still elect to prove up the charged offenses.

MANNING Your Honor. I wrote this statement in the confinement facility. The following facts are provided in support of the providence inquiry for my court-martial.
MANNING
MOUNTAIN

MANNING

MANNING I am a 25-year old Private First Class in the United States Army. I enlisted with the hope of obtaining both real world experience and earning benefits under the GI Bill for college opportunities. I told my recruiter that I was interested in geopolitical matters and information technology. He suggested that I consider becoming an intelligence analyst. I agreed.

I enjoyed the fact that an analyst could use information derived from a variety of sources to inform the command of its choices for determining the best course of action. But I quickly realized that I was neither physically nor mentally prepared for the requirements of basic training. My basic training experience lasted six months instead of the normal ten weeks.

MANNING I then reported for the Advanced Individual Training. Unlike basic training I fit in and did well. I especially enjoyed the practice of analysis using computer applications and other methods I was familiar with. Master Sergeant Adkins recognized my skills and potential and tasked me to work on the incident tracker, a tool abandoned by a previously assigned analyst. In the months preceding my upcoming deployment, I worked on creating a new version of the incident tracker and used SigActs to populate it.

SigActs give a first impression of a specific or isolated event. This event can be an improvised explosive device attack, small arms fire engagement, engagement with a hostile force, or any other event a specific unit documented and recorded in real time. The SigActs I used were from Afghanistan, because at the time our unit was scheduled to deploy to Afghanistan. Later my unit was reassigned to deploy to Eastern Baghdad, Iraq. As an analyst I viewed the SigActs as historical data. The information contained within a single SigAct or group of SigActs is not very sensitive.

AFGHANISTAN
IRAQ

MANNING WikiLeaks showed up in my daily Google search for information related to U.S. foreign policy. In one of my searches of WikiLeaks, I found the United States Army Counter Intelligence Center. After reviewing the report, I continued my research and discovered information that contradicted the report, including information indicating that WikiLeaks, similar to other press agencies, seemed to be dedicated to exposing illegal activities and corruption. WikiLeaks received numerous awards and recognition for its reporting.

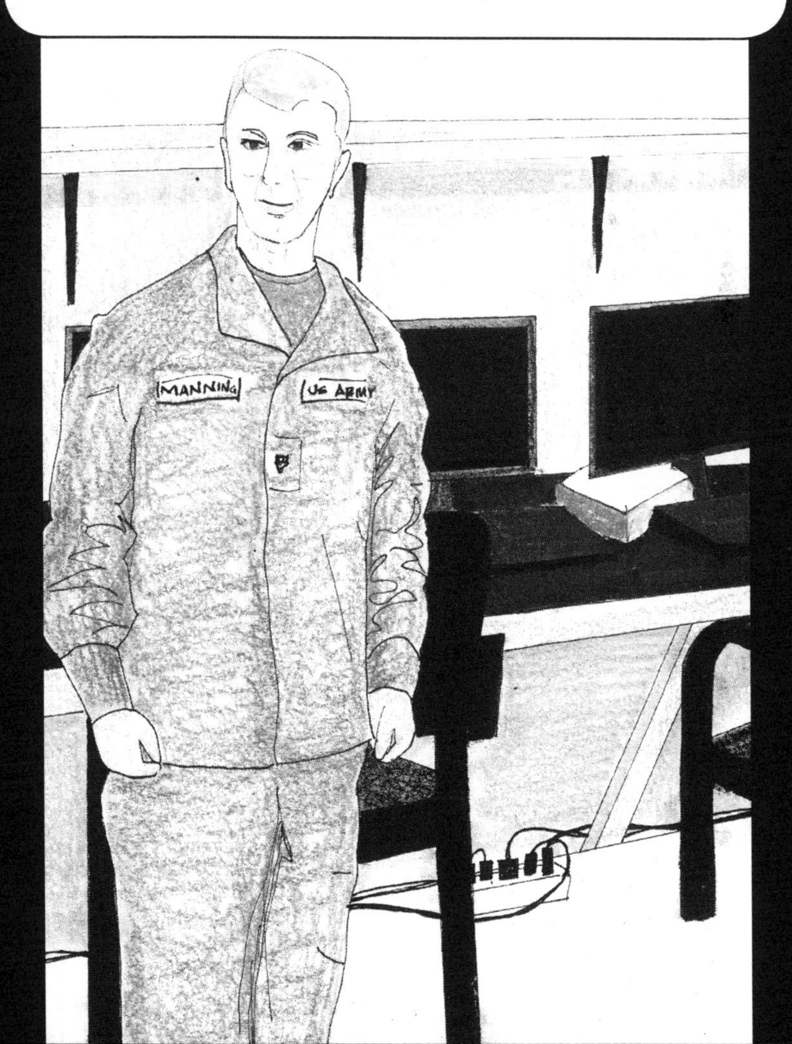
MANNING
US ARMY

MANNING In addition to visiting the WikiLeaks website, I began following WikiLeaks using Instant Relay Chat sometime in early January 2010. Over a period of time I became more involved in these discussions, especially when conversations turned to geopolitical events and information technology topics, such as networking and encryption methods. The conversations allowed me to feel connected to others even when alone. They helped me pass the time and keep motivated throughout the deployment.

THE RELEASES BEGIN

MANNING I created copies of the SigAct tables as part of the process of backing up information. At the time, I did not intend to use this information for any purpose other than for backup. I later decided to release this information publicly. I still believe that these tables are two of the most significant documents of our time. I planned to take them with me on mid-tour leave and decide what to do with them. At some point prior to my leave, I transferred the information from my computer to a Secure Digital memory card for my digital camera.

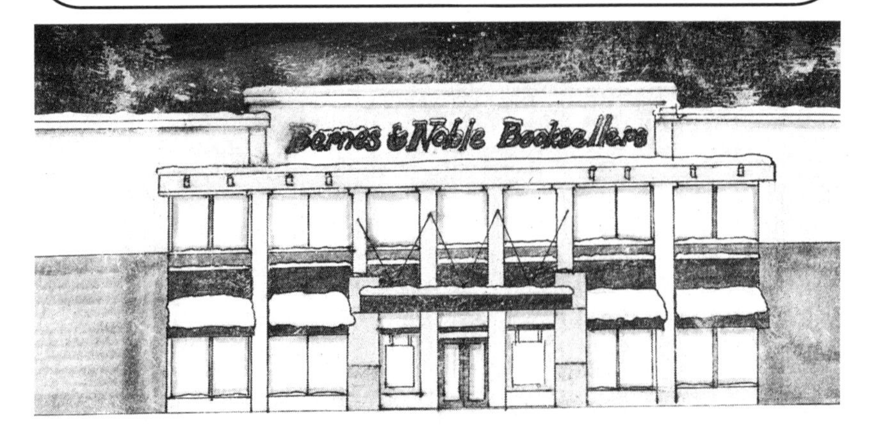
Barnes & Noble Booksellers

Manning uploaded the SigActs to WikiLeaks from a Barnes & Noble in Rockville, MD.

MANNING When I began mid-tour leave on 23 January 2010, a blizzard bombarded the mid-Atlantic. I spent a significant period of time stuck inside the home of my aunt, Debra Van Alstyne, in Potomac, Maryland. I began to think about what I knew and the information I still had in my possession.

The SigActs represented the on-the-ground reality of both conflicts in Iraq and Afghanistan. We were risking so much for people that seemed unwilling to cooperate with us, leading to frustration and anger on both sides. I began to become depressed with the situation. In attempting to conduct counterterrorism and counterinsurgency operations we became obsessed with capturing and killing human targets on lists.

If the public had the SigActs, it could spark a debate on the role of the military and our foreign policy. Detailed analysis of the data over time might cause our society to reevaluate counterterrorism and counterinsurgency operations that ignore the complex dynamics of people living in the affected environment every day.

MANNING I decided to try to expose the SigActs to an American newspaper.
The Washington Post
A reporter at the *Post* informed me that they would possibly be interested but that such decisions were made only after seeing the information and consideration by the senior editors.
The New York Times
I called the public editor at the *Times* and left a message stating I had access to information about Iraq and Afghanistan that I believed was very important. Despite leaving my phone number and personal email address, I never received a reply.

MANNING After these failed efforts I ultimately decided to submit the materials to WikiLeaks. Based upon my research this seemed the best medium within my reach for publishing this information to the world. I considered my options one more time. I felt that the right thing to do was to release the SigActs.

I visited the WikiLeaks website, followed the prompts, and sent the compressed data files of CIDNE-I (for Iraq) and CIDNE-A (for Afghanistan) SigActs through Tor, software which routes Internet traffic through a network of servers and other Tor clients in order to conceal the user's location and identity. I left the SD card in a camera case at my aunt's house in the event I needed it again in the future.

I returned from mid-tour leave. Although the information had not yet been published, I felt this sense of relief by them having it. I felt I had accomplished something that allowed me to have a clear conscience based upon what I had seen and read about and knew was happening in both Iraq and Afghanistan everyday.

Tor

MANNING During mid-February 2010, Specialist Jihrleah Showman and others at FOB Hammer discussed a video depicting several individuals being engaged by an aerial weapons team.
One of them has a weapon.
Light 'em all up.
Dead bastards!
I wanted to learn what happened and whether there was any background to the events.

MANNING I found several news accounts reporting two Reuters employees were killed during the engagement. Reuters had requested a copy of the video under the Freedom of Information Act to understand what had happened and to improve their safety practices in combat zones. They believed there was a compelling need for the immediate release of the video. Central Command told Reuters that the video might no longer exist.

207
Picking up bodies and weapons. Come on, let us shoot!
RECORDING

It was clear to me that the event happened because the aerial weapons team mistakenly identified Reuters employees as a potential threat and that the people in the van were merely attempting to assist the wounded.

MANNING Within minutes, the aerial weapons team crew learns that children were in the van. The crew exhibits no remorse.

It's their fault for bringing their kids into a battle.

Later in a particularly disturbing manner, the aerial weapons team crew verbalizes enjoyment at the sight of one of the U.S. military ground vehicles driving over a body—one of the bodies.

The most alarming aspect of the video, however, was the seemingly delightful bloodlust of the crew. At one point in the video there is a seriously wounded individual on the ground attempting to crawl to safety. Instead of calling for medical attention to the location, one of the crew members verbally asks for the wounded person to pick up a weapon so that he can have a reason to engage. For me, this seems similar to a child torturing ants with a magnifying glass.

MANNING For me it's all a big mess, and I am left wondering what these things mean. It burdens me emotionally. I planned on providing this video to Reuters to assist them in preventing events such as this in the future. Another story I found written a year later explained Reuters still had not received a formal response in accordance with Freedom of Information Act.

Namir Noor-Eldeen, freelance photojournalist killed in the attack
Saeed Chmagh's son grieves the death of his father, a Reuters driver and camera assistant.
After releasing the video, I was concerned about how it would be received. I wanted the American public to know that not everyone in Iraq and Afghanistan are targets to neutralize, but rather people struggling to live in the pressure cooker environment of what we call asymmetric warfare.

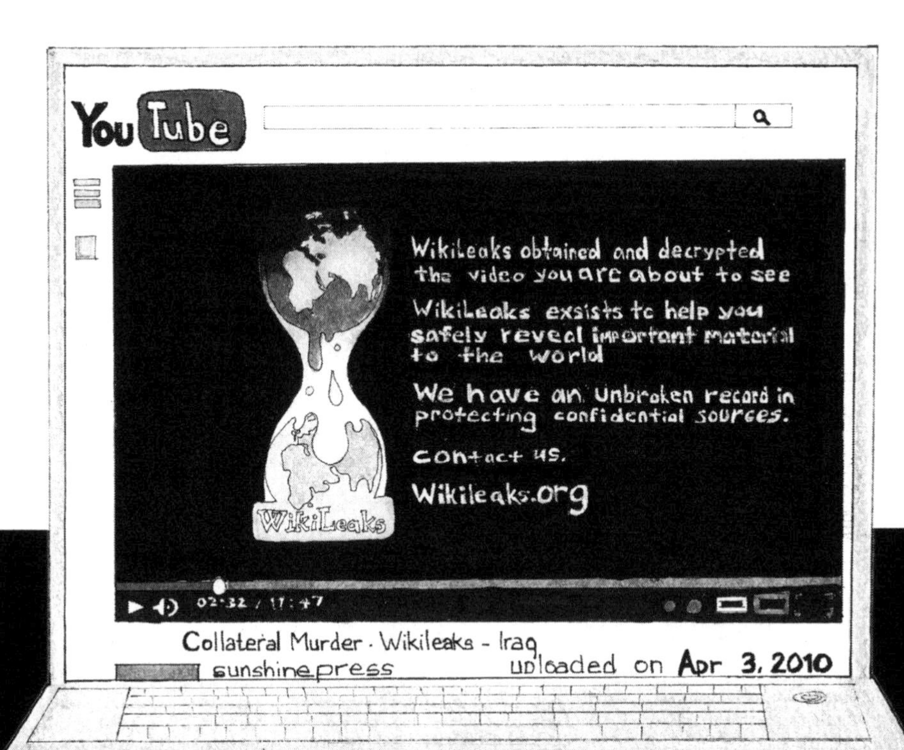
You Tube
Wikileaks obtained and decrypted the video you are about to see
Wikileaks exsists to help you safely reveal important material to the world
We have an unbroken record in protecting confidential sources.
contact us.
Wikileaks.org
WikiLeaks
02:32 / 17:47
Collateral Murder - Wikileaks - Iraq
sunshinepress
uploaded on Apr 3, 2010

12 JUL 07
CZ ENGAGEMENT
ZONE 30 GC
REUTERS FOIA REQUEST
SECRET

MANNING As I hoped, others were just as troubled as me, if not more so, by what they saw. I began seeing reports claiming that the Department of defense could not confirm the video's authenticity. Around this time, I burned a second CD-RW containing the video. I placed a classification sticker and wrote "Reuters FOIA REQ" on its face. I placed the CD-RW in one of my personal CD cases. I planned on mailing it to Reuters after I re-deployed, so they could have a copy that was unquestionably authentic.

MANNING At the same time, I began sifting through information from Joint Task Force Guantanamo, Cuba. As I digested the information, I found the Detainee Assessment Briefs. I have always been interested in the moral efficacy of our actions there. On the one hand, I have always understood the need to detain and interrogate individuals who might wish to harm the United States and our allies.

CAMP DELTA
JTF GUANTANAMO
HONOR BOUND TO DEFEND FREEDOM

Yet it seemed that we found ourselves holding indefinitely an increasing number of individuals that we believed or knew to be innocent, low-level foot soldiers that did not have useful intelligence and would be released if they were held in theater.

MANNING I also recall President Barack Obama stated that he would close Guantanamo, and that the facility diminished our "moral authority." After familiarizing myself with the Detainee Assessment Briefs, I agree.

I assessed that they were intended to provide very general background information on each of the detainees, and not a detailed assessment—and thus not very important from either an intelligence or a national security standpoint.

MANNING With my insatiable interest in geopolitics I became fascinated with the diplomatic cables published on the Department of State's Net-Centric Diplomacy server. I read not only the cables on Iraq, but also about countries and events I found interesting.
truth
truth
truth
HURLEY
MANNING
I thought these cables were a prime example of a need for a more open diplomacy. Given the fact that most of the cables were unclassified, I believed that the public release of these cables would not damage the United States. I did believe, however, that the cables might be embarrassing, since they represented very honest opinions and statements behind the backs of other nations and organizations.
No one associated with WikiLeaks pressured me into giving more information. The decisions to send documents and information to WikiLeaks were my own, and I take full responsibility.

MANNING In the military we have rules and regulations and structures designed to safeguard sensitive information, whether it be classified or unclassified. I circumvented those. I'm not the right pay-grade to make these decisions.

LIND Basically, you go against the law because you believe it is for a greater good. Is that kind of describing what you did a little bit?

MANNING Yes, your Honor.

APRIL 10, 2013

LIND There has been a violation of the court's rules. After the last session, an audio broadcast was placed on the Internet of Manning's statement that was read during his Providence Inquiry. I remind you that phones and recording devices are not allowed in the media operations center. I have not ordered persons in the media operation center to be screened for phones and recording devices. I hope I don't have to. I trust you will all follow the court's rules and we will not have any additional violations.

1775
STATES ARMY
1775

MAY 21, 2013

During the final pretrial hearing, nearly twelve weeks after Manning's Providence Inquiry, Judge Lind rules Manning's plea permissible. Now the whistle-blower cannot be found entirely "not guilty" and faces up to 21 years in prison for his lesser offenses. Unsatisfied, the government announces its intention to pursue the greater offenses for all but one minor charge.

The prosecution expects as much as 30 percent of the trial to be closed due to "the volume of classified information." At the behest of the defense, the court explores alternatives to closed testimony during the general court-martial—but does so in a closed session. During the "dry run," a government witness testifies using code words for classified information, as if the proceedings were open to the public. Judge Lind rules that the attempt to avoid future closed sessions could not "elicit coherently nuanced" testimony. Two dozen of the government's witnesses will therefore testify in partially closed proceedings during the upcoming general court-martial.

LIND While the court is not in a position to rule on any objections to specific evidence at this time, the court will address particular objections as they are raised during the trial.

The first day of the trial arrives, over three years after Manning's arrest at FOB Hammer. Manning's supporters—including notables Chris Hedges and Dr. Cornel West—fill the small gallery, which during some pretrial hearings held no more than a half-dozen attendees.

Those who can't fit in the overflow trailer spill into the 500-seat theater. The Saturday prior, more than 1,000 of Manning's supporters marched the half-mile around the perimeter of Ft. Meade.

RELEASE BRADLEY MANNING
FREE
NO SECRET TRIAL
PROTECT THE TRUTH
COURAGE
BRAD IS MY HERO
Truth on Trial
THANK YOU BRADLEY
HERO

A military policeman makes the supporters turn their "Truth" t-shirts inside out. The court's military legal expert would later weakly explain to reporters that the MP thought the t-shirts, provided by the Private Manning Support Network, would create tensions with those on the other side of Manning's case.

OPENING STATEMENTS

Capt. Jo Dean Morrow, for the prosecution:

MORROW This is not a case about an accidental spill of classified information. This, Your Honor, is a case about a soldier who systematically harvested hundreds of thousands of documents from classified databases and dumped that information on to the Internet and into the hands of the enemy. Material he knew, based on training and experience, could put the lives and welfare of his fellow soldiers at risk. This is a case of arrogance meeting access to sensitive information.

"if you had unprecedented access to classified networks 14 hours a day 7 days a week for 8+ months, what would you do?"
- "bradass87"
21 May 2010

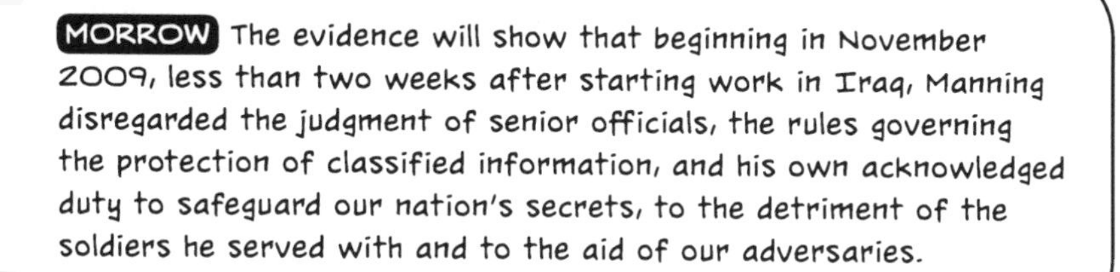
MORROW The evidence will show that beginning in November 2009, less than two weeks after starting work in Iraq, Manning disregarded the judgment of senior officials, the rules governing the protection of classified information, and his own acknowledged duty to safeguard our nation's secrets, to the detriment of the soldiers he served with and to the aid of our adversaries.
Manning used his military training to gain the notoriety he craved. In short, the evidence will show that he knew the consequences of his actions and disregarded that in his own self-interest.
Manning systematically and indiscriminately harvested more than 700,000 government records from various databases and transmitted the information, without any appropriate limits, to random opportunists.
US
US
MORROW

MORROW At every step in the process Manning attempted to hide what he was doing from others. He repeatedly moved CDs containing classified information from his workstation to his housing unit. Manning packaged, encrypted and transmitted the information using tools designed to ensure he would not be caught. After transmitting the information, Manning often took painstaking steps to erase any evidence of what he had done.
MORROW
Manning did not discriminate with gathering documents. His interest was bulk information. Manning's mastery of an unauthorized software program known as Wget aided his massive downloads. This massive amount of information holds great value for our enemies.

David Coombs, for the defense:

COOMBS It was 24 December 2009: Manning was 22 years young, in Iraq, his first deployment. He was excited to be there, to achieve his mission, and hopefully make Iraq a safer place. The alert that went out on that day broke the silence of an otherwise calm Christmas Eve. A few tense moments later came the welcome news. Despite the lead element in the convoy being hit, no soldiers were killed or injured. Everyone started celebrating. Good news was welcome on any day, but especially on Christmas Eve.
A few minutes later came some additional news: as the lead element was driving down this road, a civilian car in front of them pulled over, as was typical, to allow the convoy to go by. The car had two adults and three children. The explosive projectile went right through that car. All five occupants were taken to the hospital, one died en route. Manning couldn't celebrate because he couldn't forget about the life lost that day. From that moment forward, Manning started a struggle. No longer could he read human reports and just see a name or number and not think about that family on Christmas Eve.
Manning is not a typical soldier. He had custom dog tags that read "Humanist." Those values are placing people first, placing value on human life. In the months leading up to the deployment, Manning engaged in a chat conversation with Lauren McNamara. They talked about Manning's humanist beliefs and about Manning feeling a huge pressure to do everything he could to help his unit.

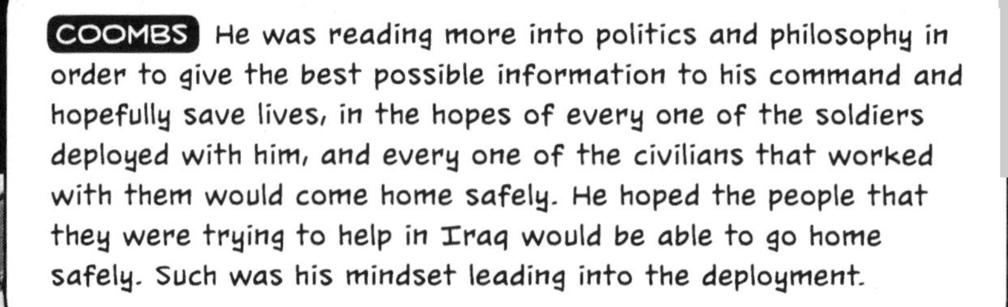
COOMBS
He was reading more into politics and philosophy in order to give the best possible information to his command and hopefully save lives, in the hopes of every one of the soldiers deployed with him, and every one of the civilians that worked with them would come home safely. He hoped the people that they were trying to help in Iraq would be able to go home safely. Such was his mindset leading into the deployment.

MANNING
BRADLEY E.
ARMY
HUMANIST

He was struggling not only with a duty to people, but also with a very private struggle about his gender. His struggles led him to feel the need to help improve what he was seeing. He started selecting information he believed that if the public saw it would make the world a better place. Information he believed could not be used against the United States.

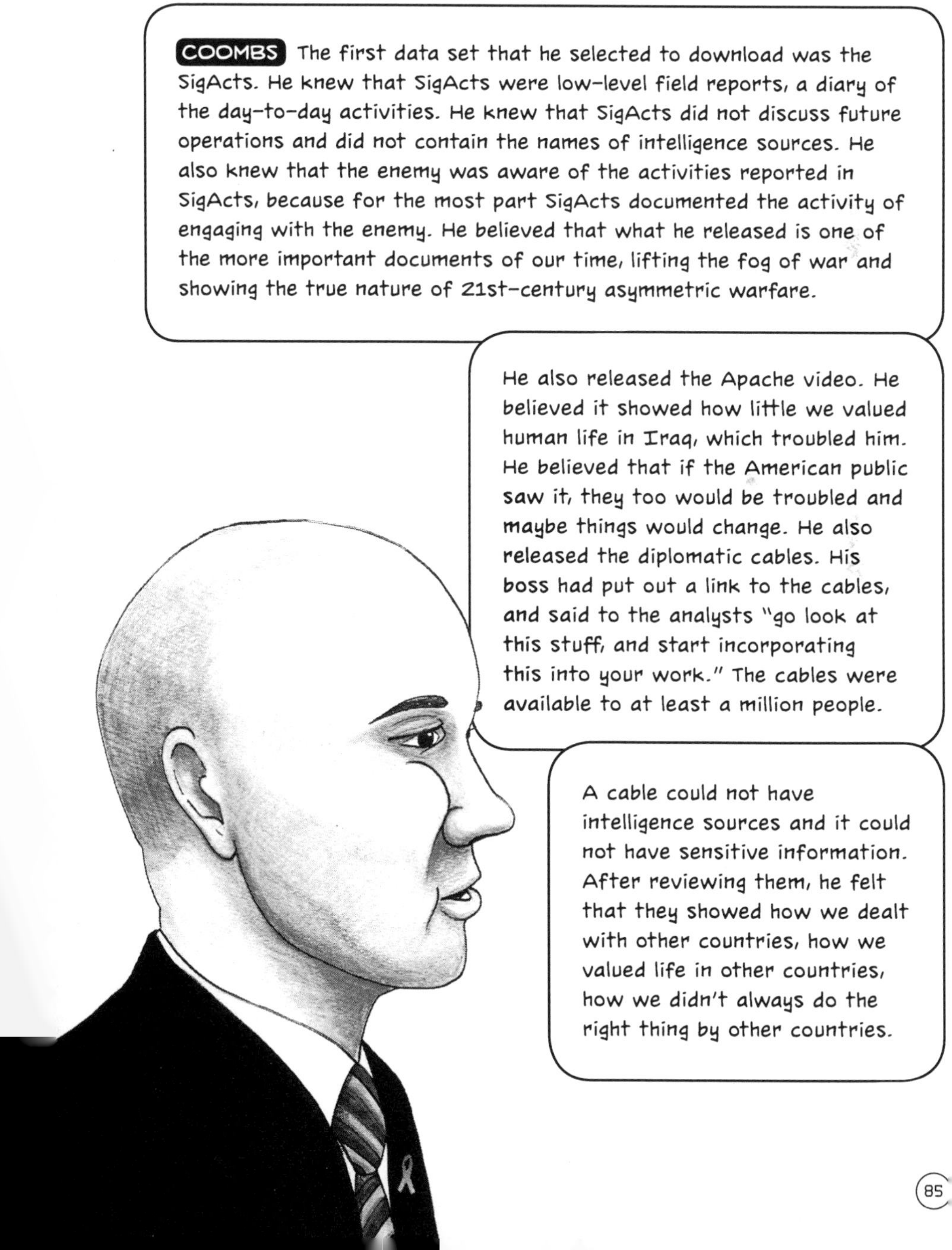

COOMBS The first data set that he selected to download was the SigActs. He knew that SigActs were low-level field reports, a diary of the day-to-day activities. He knew that SigActs did not discuss future operations and did not contain the names of intelligence sources. He also knew that the enemy was aware of the activities reported in SigActs, because for the most part SigActs documented the activity of engaging with the enemy. He believed that what he released is one of the more important documents of our time, lifting the fog of war and showing the true nature of 21st-century asymmetric warfare.

He also released the Apache video. He believed it showed how little we valued human life in Iraq, which troubled him. He believed that if the American public saw it, they too would be troubled and maybe things would change. He also released the diplomatic cables. His boss had put out a link to the cables, and said to the analysts "go look at this stuff, and start incorporating this into your work." The cables were available to at least a million people.

A cable could not have intelligence sources and it could not have sensitive information. After reviewing them, he felt that they showed how we dealt with other countries, how we valued life in other countries, how we didn't always do the right thing by other countries.

COOMBS He also released the Farah video, the Granai air strike video, and the other accompanying documents. He knew that it depicted a 2009 air attack resulting in the death of over 150 men, women, and children. He knew it received worldwide press. He had read interviews talking about what happened, why it happened and what the government was trying to do to avoid things like this in the future. The videos and documents showed why it should never have happened in the first place. He knew that there was a Freedom of Information Act request for that information, and that the Pentagon had promised to release the video but had not.

He next released the Detainee Assessment Briefs. He knew that they're mostly biographical information. He knew that most of that information had been released by the Pentagon. He knew that a lot of people were being held in Guantanamo year after year with no hope of coming into a courtroom. He knew that it might be valuable to the attorneys that were representing them, or to historians to be able to write a true account of what our nation did. Lastly, he selected the other government agency documents and the army counter-intelligence report to release.

COOMBS He chose those documents which troubled him. He believes he was selective. He had access to literally hundreds of millions of documents, and these were the documents he released. He released these documents because he was hoping to make the world a better place. He was a little naive to believe that the information that he selected could actually make a difference.

He was well-intentioned in that he selected information he hoped would make a difference. He concentrated on what the American public would think about that information, not whether the enemy would have access to it. He had absolutely no actual knowledge of whether the enemy would gain access to it.

Young, naive, but good-intentioned.

THE WITNESSES

After opening statements, the prosecution begins its case by detailing the collection of forensic evidence—including chat logs in which Manning detailed his struggles to Adrian Lamo, which the former hacker handed over to the authorities, leading to the whistle-blower's arrest.

Special Agent Toni Graham:

GRAHAM Upon receiving the chat logs we were able to corroborate as much information in there as we could. When we arrived to FOB Hammer, we briefed the chain of command basically to let them know what the allegation was, that we had obtained a search authorization and we would be collecting certain items, and that we would be affecting their normal operations for the next couple days.

Special Agent Thomas Smith:
SMITH We focused on what's depicted in that picture, two computers along the back wall there, the ones he primarily used.
I went up to each system, photographed them in place. I hit the shift key, and took a picture of the monitor. I took pictures of the cables leading in and out of the computer and conducted a hard shutdown, after which they were placed inside brown paper bags and into my backpack.

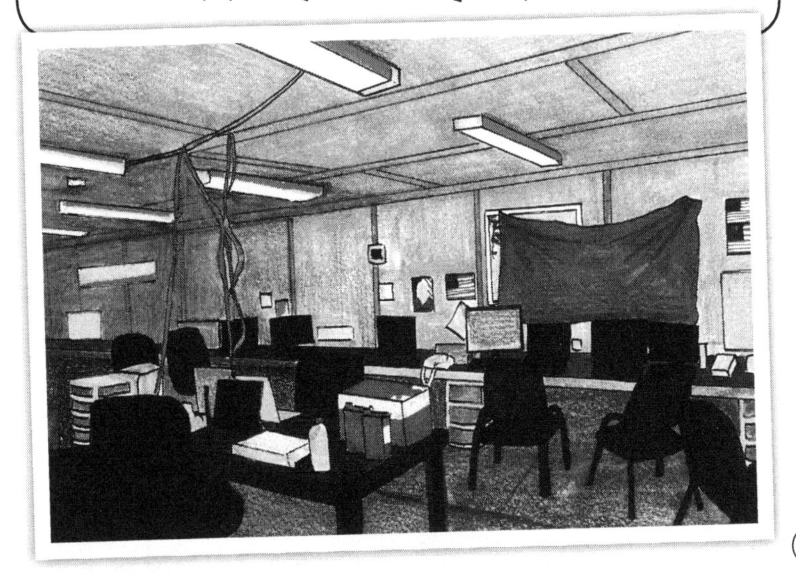

SPECIALIST ERIC BAKER He was my roommate from about November of 2009 to May 14 of 2010. He had a Mac Book Pro, a hard drive. I remember an iPod Touch, blank CDs. They came, they asked me to point out which stuff was mine and which was not mine. I told them everything on the left side of the room was mine and everything on the right side was his.

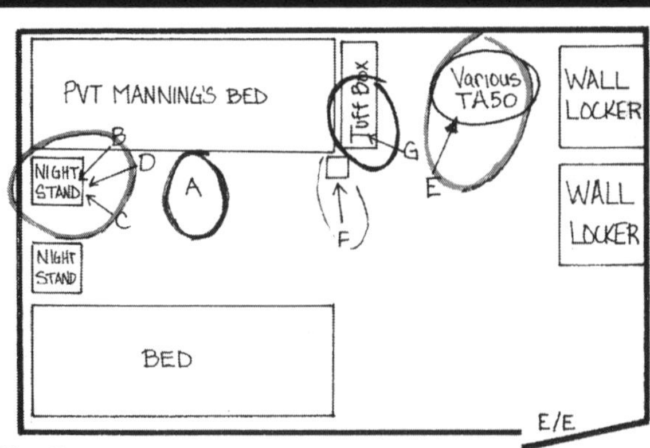

PVT MANNING'S BED
Tuff Box
Various TA50
WALL LOCKER
WALL LOCKER
NIGHT STAND
NIGHT STAND
A
B
C
D
E
F
G
BED
E/E

LEGEND
A: Apple Computer
B Two Writable CDs
C Cellular Phone
D Eight DVDs
E External Hard Drive
F CD in Box
G Camera

N
NOT TO SCALE

TITLE BLOCK
CASE NUMBER: 0160-10-CID899-14463
OFFENSE: DISCLOSURE OF CLASSIFIED INFORMATION
LOCATION: FOB HAMMER, IRAQ
VICTIM: US GOVERNMENT
SUBJECT: PFC MANNING
TIME/DATE: 0030/28 MAY 10
SKETCHED BY: SA THOMAS A SMITH
VERIFIED BY: SA TONI M. GRAHAM

JUNE 4, 2013

The prosecution calls Adrian Lamo, a former hacker who testifies that he chatted with Manning about the leaked information before handing over a copy of the chat logs to the Army Criminal Investigation Command and the FBI at a Starbucks in his California town.

After the government finishes, Coombs begins his relentless cross-examination of Lamo:

COOMBS Mr. Lamo, in early 2000, you committed a string of attacks against several large companies?

You were 22 years old at the time that you plead guilty? Same age that Manning was when he started the IM chat with you?

After contacting law enforcement you continued to chat with Manning? You also saw him as well-intentioned? He told you during your conversation that he wanted to disclose this information for public good? You saw a young 22-year-old with good intentions, much like you were? In fact, you were a supporter of LGBT?

COOMBS You also were aware that Manning knew that you had donated to WikiLeaks? He said to you, he thought he would reach out to somebody like you who would possibly understand? He told you about his life and his upbringing? He also told you that he had been questioning his gender for years, but started to come to terms with that, with his gender, during the deployment? He said he was talking to you as somebody that needed moral and emotional support?

He ended up apologizing to you on several occasions for pouring out his heart to you since you were total strangers? He told you he thought that the information that he had would have an impact on entire world? He told you he did not believe in good guys versus bad guys anymore? Based upon what he saw, he told you he could not let information just stay inside? He told you that the way he separated himself from other analysts was that he cared about people? He said he was not so much scared of getting caught and facing consequences as he was of being misunderstood?

At one point you asked him what his end game was, correct? He told you, hopefully worldwide discussions, debates and reforms? At one point you asked him why he didn't just sell the information to Russia or China? He told you that the information belonged in the public domain? He was thinking that humanity could accomplish a lot, if smart people with ideas cooperated with each other?

LAMO Yes.
I was.
That is also correct.
Yes, I did.
I recall that he referenced that he was aware.
That is correct.
Yes.
Yes, he did.
Yes.
In some amount of detail, yes.
That was my speculation, yes.
Yes.
Yes.
That was correct.
That was an interpretation, yes.
Yes, I did.
Yes.
That is also correct.
Correct.
Correct.
Yes.
Correct.

COOMBS Mr. Lamo, did he say he had no loyalty to America? Did he say the American flag didn't mean anything to him? Did he say he wanted to help the enemy?

After discussing forensic evidence, the prosecution calls witnesses to testify on Manning's training and the months preceding his deployment.

Troy Moul trained Manning as an intelligence analyst:

MOUL He was trained that anything the enemy can piece together to use against us is worth protecting. It's called the World Wide Web for a reason. The biggest example I use is: your mother's maiden name, your date of birth and Social Security number. While separate they can't do a whole lot of damage, when together somebody else can start doing bad things against your name.
As a student he was very quiet, very reserved. Did not have a lot of interaction with the other students. He was very studious, always full of questions.

MOUL Some students came to me. "You may want to check this out. There's a video on YouTube with Manning explaining what we're doing." The majority of the video consisted of Private Manning talking to the camera, explaining what he was going through at the schoolhouse, some of the material we would be covering. It was all unclassified. It wasn't actual violation of information security.

Brian Madrid, then a sergeant responsible for Manning during intelligence training, on the YouTube video:

MADRID He was using buzzwords like "top secret" and "classified materials." It brought up a red flag. I was instructed to have him do some corrective training. I had him write a report. It was my first and only time having to deal with this type of thing.

COOMBS Did PFC Manning ever say anything anti-American to you?

Sergeant First Class Jose Anica:

ANICA No, sir.

COOMBS Did he ever, did you ever hear anyone report to you that Manning made any anti-American comments?

ANICA No, sir. Not that I can recall at all.

COOMBS Was Specialist Showman one of the soldiers that worked underneath you?

ANICA Yes, sir.

COOMBS Would Specialist Showman be somebody that would report information to you?

ANICA Absolutely.

Jihrleah Showman led a team of "35 Foxtrot" analysts, including Manning, from Ft. Drum to Forward Operating Base Hammer in Iraq. They worked together every day and often talked casually, though they were not without their disagreements. Showman teased Manning. He once filed a complaint against her. No one could guess at the time how this witness would later become a crucial (and vengeful) witness for the prosecution's argument that Manning aided the enemy.

SHOWMAN He indicated to me that he was very fluent in anything computer. He spoke their language. We were having issues getting access to some division portals. He indicated to me that their passwords were not complicated and he can always get through them. In the first conversation we had, he told me that he had to make sure that he scrubbed the entire Internet of anything that involved him otherwise he would not be able to receive a security clearance and join the military.

Chief Warrant Officer 2 Kyle Balonek reads aloud the non-disclosure agreement he administers to intelligence analysts during their training.
BALONEK A non-disclosure agreement is a piece of paper that states how you will handle the classified material, who it belongs to, and what could happen to you if it's disclosed to unauthorized sources.
We don't own the information that we are utilizing, and we are not allowed to go to unauthorized sources with it. After you leave the army, it's still the property of the government. You have to trust the other analyst beside you. It's literally impossible to watch someone 24 hours a day, while also conducting your own research and analysis.
But the prosecution cannot produce the NDA Manning signed for evidence. The army lost it.
US
US
BALONEK
WITNESS

Hondo Hack testifies to Manning's diligence as an intelligence analyst.

HACK I've seen a lot of organized soldiers, but not that level of detail he had in his folders. I was impressed by the organization and the structure and the information that was in them.

When analysts at FOB Hammer first saw the Apache video, Manning testified they discussed the video.

HACK ABC news came on. Their lead story was a video of Apaches flying around Baghdad and had been shooting at civilians. I had seen the video before. I was surprised now to see it on ABC news.

Hack's choice to refer to the victims as "civilians" instead of "enemy combatants" is the closest thing to an admission from a uniformed witness that the Apache pilots broke the rules of engagement that day.

HACK

Throughout the trial, Manning's conviction on "Aiding the Enemy" hinges on the nature of WikiLeaks and whether Manning had "actual knowledge" that the released information would end up in the hands of the enemies of the United States.

COOMBS In the January to May 2010 time frame, did your unit have any actual knowledge as to which Websites enemies went to get information?

CAPTAIN CASEY FULTON General knowledge that they visit, you know, all sorts of Websites seeking information, but . . .

COOMBS But any actual knowledge as to which Websites?

FULTON They were frequently briefed on social networking sites that obviously a lot of people put personal information on.

COOMBS Anything where there's actual confirmation they may go to *this* website?

FULTON Not that I know.

US

Forensic expert David Shaver testifies on Wget common civilian software, available for free, that allows the user to easily retrieve files from the Internet. Manning, familiar with the program, used it to download the nearly 700,000 files he released. The government charges Wget was unauthorized software, and goes on to conflate unauthorized software with unauthorized access.

LIND What did you use the Army Gold Master's program to determine?
SHAVER We would use that to determine what are the authorized programs, the army programs commonly available to the users on the army network. WGet was never part of those.
LIND Does that program say that if it's not on here, you can't use it or you can't put it on the computer?

SHAVER No ma'am. That would be considered a Certificate of Networthiness (CoN). That would be the final authority on what's authorized and what's unauthorized.

LIND Assume I'm a computer user. How do I go about obtaining a CoN?

SHAVER You would put in a request to use a piece of software on the army network. They would evaluate it to make sure it meets certain criteria, whether you have to pay for it, what it does on the network, does it create a vulnerability. Then they would eventually get back to you and say yes or no.

LIND Are you aware of any specific authorization of or prohibition of Wget?

SHAVER When I looked at the Certificate of Networthiness, Wget was not on that list.

After the court learns of Wget's capability to handle large amounts of information, Chad Madaras, a fellow analyst who shared a work computer with Manning at FOB Hammer, insinuates Manning "systematically harvested" documents.

MADARAS The computer used to crash on a regular basis or operate really slowly to the point where it was difficult to get any work done. When I'd log on to the computer, it would run really slow. Wouldn't really load up anything that I was trying to use to complete my work, and then sometimes it would just completely crash right off the bat at the beginning of my shift.
I'd get our contractor to work on the machine. He'd usually have to re-image the system. I asked Manning to try to remove some of the unneeded documents off his desktop, and I also did so myself. It would take about 2 hours of my work schedule to figure out what was wrong with it.

The prosecution, over objections from the defense, prompts Sheila Glenn, a senior analyst with Army Counterintelligence, to recapitulate a 2008 report on the perceived threat WikiLeaks poses to the United States Army:

GLENN WikiLeaks is an organization that exposes illegal activity. WikiLeaks.org is knowingly encouraging criminal activities such as the theft of data, documents, proprietary information, and intellectual property, possible violation of national security laws regarding sedition and espionage, and possible violation of civil laws.

It must be presumed that WikiLeaks have or will receive sensitive or classified documents in the future. It must also be presumed that foreign adversaries will review and assess any classified information posted on WikiLeaks.org.

We know that intelligence organizations and terrorist groups perform open-source intelligence, but we cannot confirm if they actually visit that site and looked at the information. We know they have certain key words they use to search with. We know that they visit Websites.

JUNE 11, 2013

It is clear that the government considers WikiLeaks a lawless and reckless danger to national security. But Staff Sergeant Matthew Hosburgh attended a 2009 meeting of hackers and activists, for research purposes, and found a different story.

COME BACK
HOSBURGH WikiLeaks was one of the main presenters. Julian Assange gave the talk, explaining WikiLeaks, their intentions, the launch of their new site, and what the system provided.

HURLEY He did not mention terrorism in his presentation?

HOSBURGH Not that I can recall.

HURLEY Or a desire to help terrorists?

HOSBURGH No.

HURLEY WikiLeaks was focused on the public and the public's access to information?

HOSBURGH Yes.

HURLEY Ensuring openness?

HOSBURGH Yes.

HURLEY It wasn't exclusively focused on the United States?

HOSBURGH It wasn't.

HURLEY It wasn't exclusively focused on classified information?

HOSBURGH Correct.

HURLEY They were interested in trade secrets?

HOSBURGH Yes.

JUNE 12, 2013

MORE FORENSIC EVIDENCE

Mark Johnson, forensic expert:

JOHNSON We looked in Manning's buddy list to see who else he might have been communicating with. We identified one entry that was of interest indicating the chat account was associated with an alias of Julian Assange.

Captain Tooman, for the defense:

TOOMAN You also were able to look at or recover other Websites that Manning would have visited. None of those Websites were associated with terrorism?

JOHNSON No.

TOOMAN They weren't associated with a hatred of America or anti-American beliefs?

JOHNSON No.

WGET, AGAIN . . .

The prosecution attempts to prove Manning exceeded authorized access and violated the Computer Fraud Abuse Act.

Greg Weaver, Army Cyber Command:

WEAVER Wget is basically an application that allows you to download files or do entire content downloading of a website in an effort to gather all the information from that site. Basically mirroring a site, copying the whole site to a local drive or whatever. Technology is advancing rapidly. Policy doesn't always keep up with the technology. The user has the responsibility and it's entrusted to him not to exceed the authorities. Having accessibility doesn't equate to authorization.

TOOMAN Are you aware of whether or not it's common for systems to have unauthorized software or unauthorized files on them?

Technical director for the army's intelligence infrastructure (called the Distributed Common Ground System), Mark Kitz:

KITZ It is my understanding that it is relatively common, yes.

Captain Thomas Cherepko, an officer in charge of maintaining the brigade's network at FOB Hammer:
CHEREPKO There was a command laxity about enforcing this.
U.S.
U.S.
CHEREPKO

Jason Milliman, a contractor who serviced the computers in Manning's SCIF:

MILLIMAN A user could install the executable file on the desktop without coming to me even though it wouldn't be authorized. I didn't go behind every user on a daily basis to find out if they had installed something. It was understood, or I thought it was understood that we're all in a position of trust so that was not something that was normally done.

He said, "If people knew what I did with computers, they would be amazed." He seemed kind of serious and kind of joking at the same time. I didn't know how to take him.

JUNE 17, 2013

Testimony continues to circle around how Manning used or misued his access to information. Here, army engineers testify about the Global Address List, containing 74,000 email addresses for soldiers stationed in Iraq. The government has charged Manning with Stealing U.S. Government Property.

Chief Warrant Officer Ronald Nixon:

NIXON It's not a public consumption piece. It's not a user function to be able to download the Global Address List as a whole.
TOOMAN But has there ever been any directive that said you can't download e-mail addresses off the Global Address List?
Chief Warrant Officer Armond Rouillard:
ROUILLARD There has not. It goes to intent. We don't write the rules for everything. But why do you need that much data?

JUNE 18, 2013

WHAT IS "CLOSELY HELD"?

The defense tries a distinction that could push Manning's releases outside the government's expanding umbrella of what is "closely held."

TOOMAN The actions of WikiLeaks are independent from the actions of Manning. WikiLeaks, for their actions to be relevant, would have to understand the definition of "closely held." They publish lots of things that wouldn't meet that definition. The mere publishing of it doesn't make it more likely that it was closely held. "Closely held" is something that is determined by the government.
LIND Okay. I'll determine it in this case, but okay.
US
TOOMAN

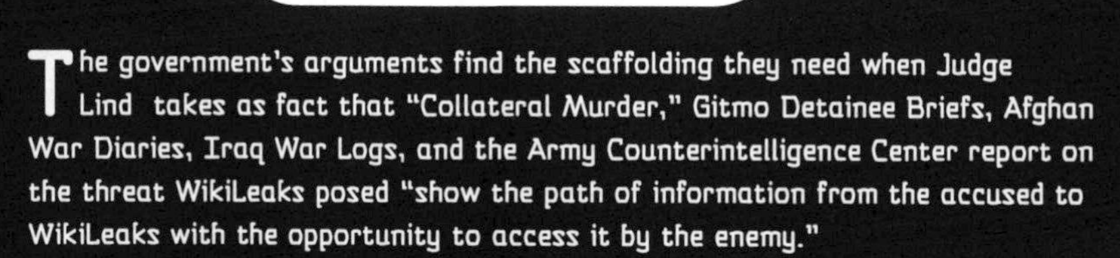

The government's arguments find the scaffolding they need when Judge Lind takes as fact that "Collateral Murder," Gitmo Detainee Briefs, Afghan War Diaries, Iraq War Logs, and the Army Counterintelligence Center report on the threat WikiLeaks posed "show the path of information from the accused to WikiLeaks with the opportunity to access it by the enemy."

What's more, the court will admit as evidence a tweet allegedly from WikiLeaks asking for "as many .mil addresses as possible." Among other testimony, Lind cites Special Agent Mander using the Wayback machine to capture the controversial tweet and authenticate it.

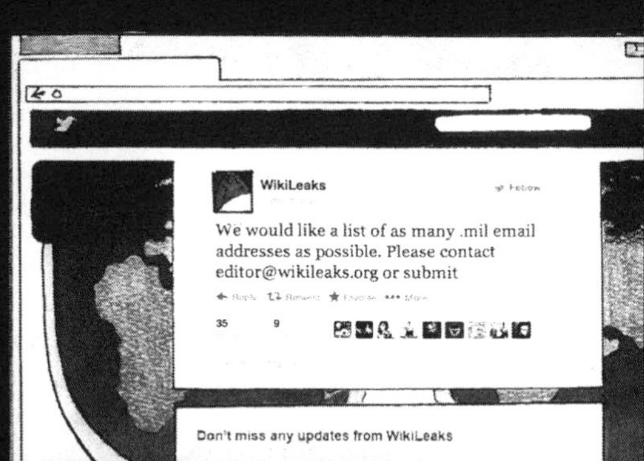

WikiLeaks
We would like a list of as many .mil email addresses as possible. Please contact editor@wikileaks.org or submit
35
9
Don't miss any updates from WikiLeaks

If Rouillard implies that it's simply the volume of information that shows Manning violated the Computer Fraud and Abuse Act (CFAA), it's the nature of information that determines the more serious charges of violating the Espionage Act and Aiding the Enemy. Classified or not, the government must prove that the information Manning released is "closely held" by the government—that is, if the government "sought to keep the information from the public."

In response, the government pursues an unusual argument: they admit that the Apache helicopter video was unclassified, but maintain it was closely held. Captain Hunter Whyte points to stipulated testimony from Jon LaRue, a seasoned Apache pilot who reviewed the video, which said it reveals "tactics, techniques and procedures" (TTPs) having to do with "the use of a laser for ranging, altitude, and air speed."

WHYTE

truth
But LaRue and the prosecution are upstaged. The defense counters with a statement from Rear Admiral Donegan of U.S. Central Command, the military command covering the entire Middle East. Donegan reviewed the video in October 2010, six months after WikiLeaks published it as "Collateral Murder," and surmised it should have been unclassified

JUNE 26, 2013

The government has elicited testimony to try and show the size and nature of the information Manning leaked. But five of the charges Manning faces allege he stole USG property worth more than $1,000, the threshold for federal larceny.

The prosecution calls multiple witnesses to testify to the monetary value of the information, but the defense bests them. The government equates the budget for the Net-Centric Diplomacy database with the value of the information stored therein. But Charles Wisecarver, chief technology officer at the State Department, admits he only ever saw inflated budget requests that "shoot for the sky."

JUNE 28, 2013

Colonel David Miller, an officer in Manning's unit, employs a twisted choice of words when he recalls the mood of his soldiers after they learned Manning leaked documents showing the horrors of the war:

MILLER I was coming back from dinner or something like that. The forensic investigators approached me and said they had been instructed to secure Manning and his computer, and that agents were coming to take him away. I was stunned.

The last thing I anticipated was an internal security breach, from one of our own. I pulled the staff together to determine what, if anything, we had or had not done that led to this. They were angry, sad, grieving, frustrated—all at the same time. It was like a funeral-like atmosphere.

US.

JULY 1, 2013

Now in its fifth week, the prosecution's case begins to draw to a close, but not without reading copious amounts of stipulated testimony into the record.

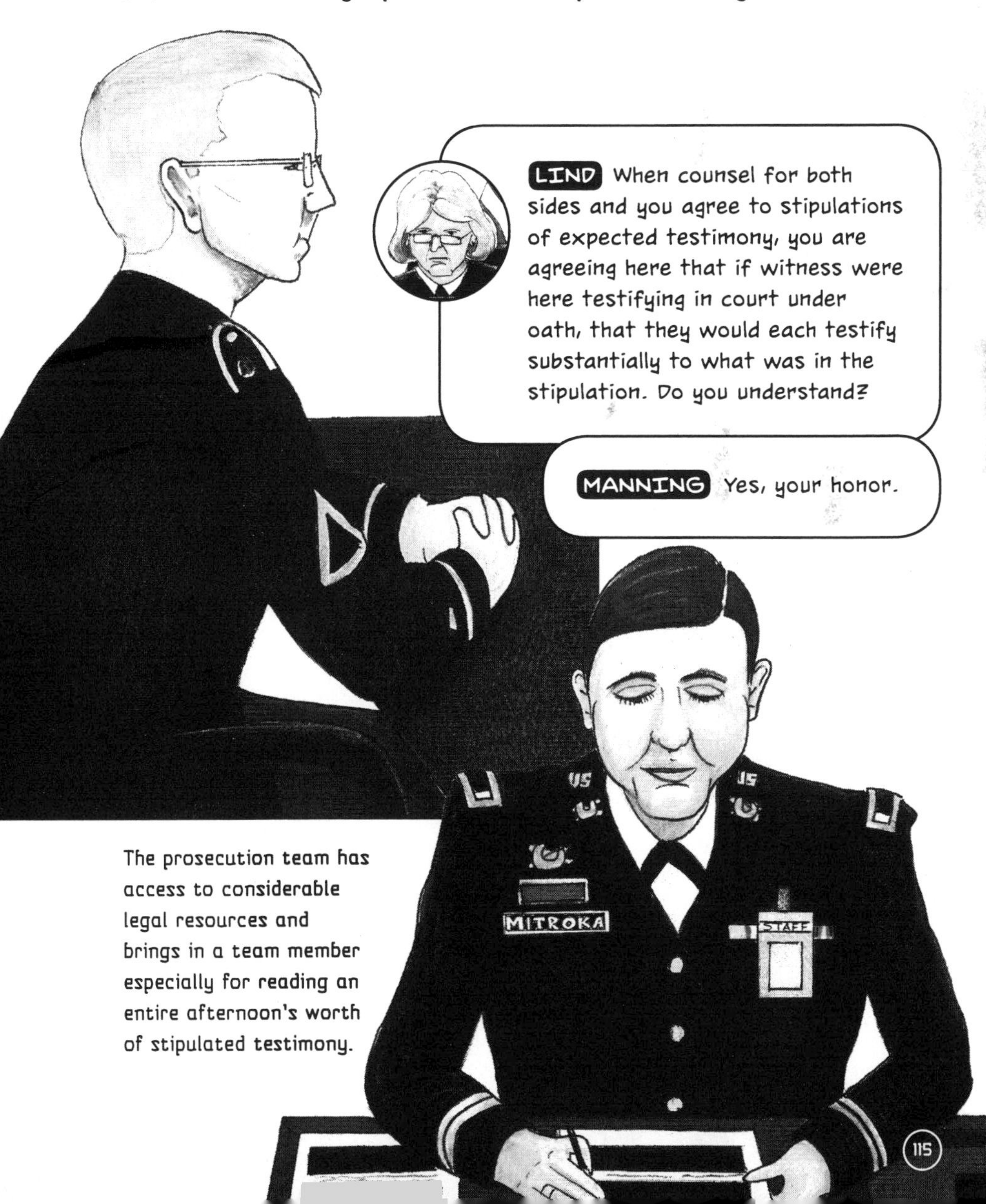
LIND When counsel for both sides and you agree to stipulations of expected testimony, you are agreeing here that if witness were here testifying in court under oath, that they would each testify substantially to what was in the stipulation. Do you understand?
MANNING Yes, your honor.
MITROKA
STAFF

The prosecution team has access to considerable legal resources and brings in a team member especially for reading an entire afternoon's worth of stipulated testimony.

Unlike stipulated testimony, which can be contradicted, attacked or explained in the same way as if the person were testifying here in person, stipulated fact is that which both sides agree is fact. The prosecution reads stipulated facts about the raid on Osama bin Laden's compound, the starting point of their argument that Manning delivered information relating to national security to enemies of the United States:

FEIN Osama bin Laden was the leader of al-Qaeda, the terrorist organization responsible for the attacks against the United States at the World Trade Center and Pentagon on 11 September 2001. On 2 May 2011, United States government officials raided Osama bin Laden's compound located in Abbottabad, Pakistan and collected several items of digital media. From them, the following items were obtained: a letter from Osama bin Laden to a member of al-Qaeda requesting the member gather Department of defense material posted to WikiLeaks; a letter from the same member of al-Qaeda to Osama bin Laden, attached to which was the Afghanistan War Logs as posted by WikiLeaks, and Department of State information released by WikiLeaks.

The remainder of the information is redacted, but it is important to remember that what's crucial to a guilty verdict on Aiding the Enemy is that Manning had actual knowledge of whether the enemy would gain access to the information he released.

Daniel Lewis, a senior defense Intelligence Agency official, worked on the case of George Tofimoff, a retired Army Reserve intelligence officer convicted in 2001 of selling 50,000 pages of classified information to the Soviet Union for $250,000. Hurley cross-examined Lewis on his ability to value the cables Manning released.

LEWIS What I said was, when you asked me if you gave me a document, could I tell you how much that would be worth, and I cannot tell you how much that document would be worth.

But after closed testimony, Judge Lind determines she cannot accept Lewis as an expert in valuing information.

FEIN
PLANAR
Afterwards, the government rests its case.

JULY 8, 2013

THE DEFENSE BEGINS ITS CASE

The Good Soldiers
David Finkel

The government has repeatedly insisted that "Collateral Murder" was "closely held" despite being unclassified, and used this distinction to advance charges against Manning. The defense enters the Apache cockpit video and a transcript of the crew's communications onto the record so that Judge Lind may compare them to a passage describing the same video in David Finkel's *The Good Soldiers*, published before Manning released the video. They match, puncturing the government's inflated argument.

Request permission to engage.
So, uh, you're free to engage. Over.
All right. We'll be engaging.
Roger, go ahead.
I'm gonna . . . I cant get 'em now because they're behind that building.

TADS
Light 'em all up.
C'mon, fire!
Keep shooting.
TADS RECORDING
ROUNDS 222
Goddamnit Kyle.
Ha Ha Ha I hit 'em.
I'm firing.
Target hit.
We'll clear the smoke.
We'll fire one more.
TADS RECORDING

The defense calls Chief Warrant Officer 2 Joshua Ehresman, an intelligence analyst who worked at FOB Hammer during Manning's deployment.

COOMBS And after the SigActs in this case were posted online in open-source, did you continue to use SigActs as intel analysts?

EHRESMAN Yes, sir.

COOMBS Did it change how you used the SigActs once they were released by WikiLeaks?

EHRESMAN No, because it's just historical information.

COOMBS And based upon your ability to view his performance, what was your assessment of Manning's work performance?

EHRESMAN He was our best analyst by far when it came to developing products. Most soldiers you would have is to spell it out exactly what they had to do. He would bounce a couple of ideas off of you and come up with exactly what you're looking for. He was our go-to guy for that stuff.

US
US

COOMBS Did PFC Manning ever come to you to complain about his belief that no one in his unit seemed to care about the mission?

SERGEANT DAVID SADTLER Yes. He showed me a translated copy of a report where Iraqi nationals had arrested a group of Iraqis or Moroccans printing "anti-Iraq government propaganda." He seemed to be concerned that they were arrested for printing a political critique. He showed it to his co-workers. I read it and I dropped the idea. When he brought that up to me, I told him that it was just what happens. We're not in the United States, so different countries have different laws and different rights. He was upset over the situation.

He had a deep belief in news and what was going on, whereas other people were more concerned about just going throughout their day.
WITNESS
SADTLER

COOMBS Now, I want to ask you about the Net-Centric Diplomacy database. Do you know how analysts were informed of their access to diplomatic cables?

Captain Steven Lim, under whom Manning worked:

LIM I do. Through myself. I gave the link to all of my analysts to kind of broaden their horizons and kind of get rid of their tunnel vision of looking at just what the enemy is doing on the ground. We need to take a step back and look at the larger picture, specifically with reconciliation in Iraq.

COOMBS Did you say, for example, only look at cables that deal with Iraq?

LIM I did not, no.

COOMBS Did you or anyone in the your section put out any guidance or restrictions on what an analyst could and could not download from the Net-Centric Diplomacy Database?

LIM No, Sir.

COOMBS How about the manner in which you downloaded information?

LIM No, Sir.

JULY 9, 2013

COOMBS The defense calls Ms. Lauren McNamara to the stand.

Manning sought out McNamara, formerly Zachary Antolak, through her YouTube videos in which she discussed, as she puts it, "subjects such as atheism, religion, politics, civil rights, and sometimes, mathematics and computer science information theory." They chatted for seven months during 2009.

MCNAMARA We were just a couple of people talking about our lives and he just shared various experiences and interests. He often had interesting things to say about his job and what that entailed and his interest in politics, world affairs and things like that and he seemed to have some very well-informed and complex opinions. It seemed like he just wanted someone to talk to about these things on the same level.

The defense moves to admit the chat logs as evidence to demonstrate Manning's "then-existing state of mind" when he released classified documents. The government objects, calling it hearsay (something which didn't bother them when admitting chat logs between Manning and Adrian Lamo into evidence). Instead, Coombs suggests he go over the relevant sections with McNamara during testimony.

COOMBS Can you read that section where he talked about delving more into philosophy books?

MCNAMARA "8:07 p.m. bradass87: same thing with me, I'm reading a lot more. Delving deeper into philosophy, arts, physics, biology, politics than I ever did in school. What's even better with my current position is I can apply what I learn to provide more information to my officers and commanders and hopefully save lives."

LIND All right. Government, you have a hearsay objection. Why do you believe that that does not go towards then-existing state of mind?

OVERGAARD A general statement about what the accused is reading, that he thinks he can apply that to his officers and hopefully save lives, it just—it doesn't seem to be relevant to the—

LIND So now you have a relevance objection?

OVERGAARD Yes, ma'am. On top of the hearsay objection.

LIND All right. I mean—I'm going to overrule the relevance objection. Go ahead.

Coombs and McNamara discuss two more sections which Judge Lind finds acceptable. The prosecution relents, withdraws its objection, and the court admits the chat logs as evidence for Manning's then state of mind

OVERCLASSIFICATION IS THE PROBLEM

Retired Colonel Morris Davis, former chief prosecutor for the Guantanamo military commissions qualifies as an expert on Guantanamo detainee policy, over the objections of the prosecution.

COOMBS Did you reach any conclusions in this case concerning whether the charged Guantanamo Detainee Assessment Briefs could reasonably be expected to cause damage to the national security of the United States?

DAVIS If you studied open-source material, you could sit down and write what would be a substantially verbatim version of the Detainee Assessment Briefs. It was basically biographical information about each of the detainees. There's no actionable intelligence in the detainee assessment briefs.

One of the fundamental problems is everything is presumptively classified and getting it back out of that wicket is difficult. Other than causing embarrassment to the country, I don't see how the enemy could gain anything of value from reading the detainee assessment. If you are trying to achieve some strategic tactical advantage, the Detainee Assessment Briefs is not the place to get it.

And so the defense continues to build its case that much of the information Manning leaked was over-classified.

Cassius Hall, of U.S. Army Intelligence and Security Command, offers a similar opinion on the SigActs.

HALL We individually reviewed the SigActs and then compared them again with the Original Classification Authority's determination. A lot of the information, you can find in the open-source. Like, if a soldier was killed in Afghanistan, the SigAct had the soldier's name, but you can basically find that on the DOD website. Or when you deploy to an area, it's probably no secret because the locals will already know.

COOMBS In this instance, are you disagreeing with the OCA that reviewed the charge SigActs?

HALL No, sir.

COOMBS What are you doing then?

HALL You may disagree with something when you're behind closed doors, but the commander says "This is what I want." So you drive on. So I don't have—it's not our information, so . . .

Charles Ganiel, a security specialist with the army, made similar comparisons between the State Department cables and open-sources.

COOMBS And how many of the cables were you able to find open-source information on?

GANIEL I believe it was all but probably two of the cables.

COOMBS And based upon the information that you found, did you reach any conclusions about the charge cables?

GANIEL I just felt that a lot of the information was already out in the public domain by doing my research. But if the Original Classification Authority says it's secret, that's how you treat it.

OVERGAARD You said open-source information existed on all but two of the cables?

GANIEL I'm pretty sure it was all but two.

OVERGAARD That was just the general factual information?

GANIEL Right. Nothing is word-for-word. It could be a couple words here, couple words there.

OVERGAARD And did you find any information in open-source where the government confirmed any of the classified information in the cables?

GANIEL No.

OVERGAARD And you never found in any of them all of the information that was in the cables?

GANIEL No.

THE DEFENSE'S KEY WITNESS

Professor Yochai Benkler takes the stand to testify on the nature of WikiLeaks. The courtroom fills with spectators ready to hear how Benkler and the defense will try to convince Judge Lind that WikiLeaks is a legitimate journalistic organization.

COOMBS Have you ever conducted any research and writing on what is called "the Networked Fourth Estate"?

BENKLER Yes, absolutely. I've been working generally on the influence of the Internet on democracy since the mid-'90s.

COOMBS Can you give a general description of the Networked Fourth Estate?

BENKLER It is the set of practices, organizing models, and technologies that together fill the role that in the 20th century we associated with the free press. The Fourth Estate is the way in which the press provides a public check on the three branches of government. The Networked Fourth Estate is essentially the cluster of practices and technologies and organizations that fill that role in the 21st-century model of network information production.

COOMBS When did you begin your research for "A Free Irresponsible Press: WikiLeaks and the Battle Over the Soul of the Networked Fourth Estate," published in the *Harvard Civil Liberties Review*?

BENKLER Right after the release of the helicopter video. I was intrigued. When this came out it was clear Reuters had been trying to access the footage for two years using traditional means. This seemed like an interesting connection between network models and traditional media. And it was released in the National Press Club, which provided a bridge between new media and old media.

MORROW Your Honor, this is a distinguished academic and obviously a very smart man, but the government's position is that the scope of the Networked Fourth Estate, or at least how he's described it now, is somewhat disassociated from his opinions about WikiLeaks, whether they're a journalist organization.

National Press Club
NATIONAL PRESS CLUB

LIND I'm not quite sure I understand that.

MORROW Well, I'm not quite sure I understand the Networked Fourth Estate, but . . .

LIND Professor Benkler, am I understanding you correctly in saying that you're basically looking at, you know, in the last century with traditional news media the way people got news was through newspapers. As technology evolved, more people on the Internet are sharing things?

BENKLER That's at the core of it.

LIND But you're studying the evolution of how people get news or develop news?

BENKLER Yes, yes.
LIND Well Captain Morrow, I assume he's going to be testifying about how WikiLeaks fits into the Networked Fourth Estate.

MORROW I guess you can see how the testimony goes and we can raise additional objections to its relevance as they come.
LIND All right. I'll go ahead and accept him as an expert in that area.

COOMBS Based upon your research, what type of organization is WikiLeaks?
BENKLER WikiLeaks is a—
MORROW Objection, Your Honor. We would ask that the scope of his testimony be limited to the time period from 2007 to March 2010.

LIND Mr. Coombs, what is the relevance of what WikiLeaks is after the charged offenses and publications?

COOMBS Because the government's argument in this case is that by giving information to WikiLeaks, PFC Manning gave information to the enemy. The government's whole argument seems to be premised on painting WikiLeaks as a bad organization, and Julian Assange as a bad person. That train of thought is really created after March 2010.

That is why the defense believes Professor Benkler should be allowed to talk about how the trend changed from viewing WikiLeaks as a source of legitimate journalistic information to now being public enemy number one. The government is trying to lump my client with that in order to argue that he aided the enemy.

LIND Go ahead with your questioning.

COOMBS So, Professor Benkler—

FEIN Ma'am, can the government still be heard on this? First of all, there's no evidence that PFC Manning knew any of this, which speaks to the relevancy of this entire thing—
LIND All right, government, I don't agree. I see the relevance of the type of journalistic organization, if WikiLeaks is one. Go ahead, defense.
COOMBS Based upon your research, what conclusions again did you reach about WikiLeaks as an organization?
BENKLER WikiLeaks provides a solution for how network journalism can stabilize leak-based investigative journalism in the face of diminishing newsrooms, many more organizations, and a much less well-structured way of defending it in court.

COOMBS Did WikiLeaks have a published mission statement prior to April 2010?

BENKLER Yes. Their mission statement was primarily focused on exposing the corruption and unethical behavior of authoritarian governments in Asia, former Soviet countries, and some countries in Africa. But in the mission statement they also said they would support exposures of unethical behaviors by people everywhere in every country.

COOMBS And how did WikiLeaks go about trying to expose unethical practices, illegal behavior and wrongdoing within corrupt corporations and governments?

BENKLER They created a safe platform for people who were close to the materials, who had knowledge on the inside to leak materials for public revelation.

Before 2010, such public revelations included internal documents from Julius Baer, a Swiss bank, which amounted to a guide to using offshore accounts for tax avoidance. A leaker also disclosed the Green Ban, an authoritarian Chinese state censorship program. The public reacted severely, and the government scrapped the program. Such work earned WikiLeaks awards from Index on Censorship in 2008 and Amnesty International in 2009.

COOMBS And based upon your overview of WikiLeaks' activities prior to April 2010, how was WikiLeaks portrayed online and in print media?

BENKLER The Julius Baer case in early 2008 was the moment when WikiLeaks was widely described in the press as a new online journalistic organization. In that case the Reporters' Committee on Freedom of the Press, Gannett Company, The Associated Press, and The Newspaper Editors Associates filed an amicus brief saying, "you can't shut this down."

COOMBS Prior to April of 2010, did you see anything to connect WikiLeaks with a terrorist organization?

BENKLER No.

COOMBS Did the portrayal of WikiLeaks start to change in 2010?

BENKLER Substantially. I'd say the shift occurred concomitant with the release of the Iraq War Logs later in 2010.

COOMBS But I want to backtrack just for a second and go back to your article. In it, you considered a 2008 Pentagon report. Did you see anything in this document that supported the idea that WikiLeaks provided information to the enemy?

BENKLER No. There were theoretical statements about how the enemy could come and use this, with a particular emphasis on how the enemy could try to use it for propaganda to inject false information and have perceptual management. Other than speculation, there was no evidence that there had actually been any use by any enemy.

What WikiLeaks has done is to professionalize the model of intake, selection and authentication. The thing that is special about WikiLeaks is that it authenticates, and fewer than 1 percent of the materials are identified as potentially authentic.

COOMBS Does anything in the report undercut WikiLeaks as an investigative journalistic organization?

BENKLER No, quite the contrary: I'd say that there are multiple references throughout the report that would lead a reasonable reader to see WikiLeaks as a journalistic organization.

WikiLeaks

After a brief recess, Lind asks both parties to set forth their respective positions.

LIND Defense, I would like you to explain to me exactly where we are going with this witness' testimony and what you plan to do with it.

COOMBS The government has offered documentation to depict WikiLeaks as an organization that PFC Manning should have known would have given information to the enemy. In fact, they have to prove he had actual knowledge that by giving it to WikiLeaks, he was providing it to the enemy. The defense's position on this is that anyone looking at WikiLeaks prior to the charged releases would have viewed it as a legitimate journalistic organization.
Additionally, the defense's position is that the enemy went to get this information only after the government's responses to the leaks. Professor Benkler's testimony also rebuts the accusation of wanton conduct by PFC Manning in releasing information to a legitimate news organization.

FEIN
LIND Government, you just heard what the defense is planning to do. What is your position?
FEIN Any evidence of the government's reaction after the commission of his offenses could be irrelevant to the charges in this case. And the government doesn't intend to argue at all about what WikiLeaks did or did not become. It's only at the time of the commission of the offenses what PFC Manning did or did not, should or should not have known.
LIND Defense, if you confine your examination to the leaks and the reactions thereafter, I will allow it.

COOMBS Professor Benkler, how did the United States respond, in general, to the publication of the Afghan SigActs?
BENKLER Admiral Mullen said WikiLeaks would have blood on its hands. Both the government and other media had no similar critique of the other organizations, of the New York Times, the Guardian, of Der Spiegel for reporting on and making available some of the war logs. The wrath was reserved purely for WikiLeaks.
The New York Times
Leaked Cables Offer a Raw Look Inside U.S. Diplomacy
The response is hard to define as anything but shrill. Secretary of State Clinton described it as an attack on the international community. Vice President Biden on a television interview said that Assange was more like a high tech terrorist.
the guardian
Massive leak of secret files exposes true Afghan war

COOMBS Is WikiLeaks a member of the Networked Fourth Estate?

BENKLER Absolutely. Journalism is made up of many things. WikiLeaks doesn't do interviews and pound the pavement, but the model of some form of decentralized leaking, that is technologically secure and allows for collaboration among different media in different countries—that's going to survive. WikiLeaks played a critical role in that particular component of what muck-raking and investigative journalism has always done.

COOMBS Thank you. No further questions.

LIND Cross-examination?

MORROW Yes, Your Honor. Now Professor Benkler, would you agree that there's a differ between the ideals of a journalist and the ide of someone seeking maximum political impact

BENKLER Not necessarily. I think journalism has a broad range. There is a relatively narro idea of mid-20th-century journalism that's very focused on just being a professional. But there's certainly politically-oriented journalism

MORROW Would that be like muck-raking journalism

BENKLER Partly. For example, if you look at somethi *The Nation*: there's a particular political worldview and oriented towards that. You select things not simply bec they're interesting but because they are relevant to ac particular political perspective. It doesn't make it not

MORROW The idea when you're a journalist is to select things that are newsworthy?
BENKLER
saying ther
forms of jc
"all the nev
to print" is

MORROW Now, would you agree that mass document leaking is somewhat inconsistent with journalism?

BENKLER No. Why would I agree with that?

MORROW If there was no news locus there?

BENKLER If it had no news and wasn't relevant I might agree, but it depends on what you're looking for. I'll give you an example. The most significant investigative organization looking at civilian casualties in the Iraq war, Iraq Body Count, used documents held by the government to show an incongruity between the number of reported civilian casualties in Iraq and the actual number known to the government from these documents. The only way you can do that is by mass analysis of lots of documents.

As a parting shot, Morrow mentions Benkler's authorship of two op-ed pieces: "Death to Whistle-Blowers" in the *New York Times*, and "The Dangerous Logic of the Bradley Manning Case" for *The New Republic*. The insinuation is plain, and plainly weak: that Benkler's published opinions on the trial discredit the validity of his legal research on democracy and the Internet.

COOMBS Professor Benkler, I want to give you an opportunity to explain those op-ed pieces. Can you tell the judge what the first was about?

BENKLER If the threat to potential whistle-blowers and leakers was as great as the death penalty or life in prison, the cost that finding Manning guilty of aiding the enemy would impose in terms of the willingness of people of good conscience but not infinite courage to come forward would severely undermine the way in which leak-based investigative journalism has worked even in the tradition of free press in the United States.
COOMBS And then the second piece?
BENKLER The logic I describe—what I call the dangerous logic—was if handing materials over to a media organization that can be read by anyone with an Internet connection means that you are handing over to the enemy—that essentially means that any leak to a media organization that can be read by any enemy anywhere in the world, becomes automatically aiding the enemy. The dangerous logic is that you essentially exclude the question of, "Have you actually gone to the enemy?"
COOMBS Thank you. No further questions.

LIND Professor Benkler, earlier you mentioned that the Fourth Estate is broad. If you, me, anyone here in the gallery had information that they weren't supposed to disclose or was protected—contract-binding information or something like that—and put it on an individual blog for the world to see, is that person now a journalist?

BENKLER This is the problem of defining a range of the journalist's privilege. As the Supreme Court wrote in *Branzburg*: the liberty of the press is the right of the lonely pamphleteer with a mimeograph, as it is for the metropolitan press with the latest technologies. It's a hard line to draw.

THE DEFENSE RESTS

truth

JULY 15, 2013

"IN A LIGHT MOST FAVORABLE TO THE PROSECUTION..."

Both the prosecution and defense have rested, but before the two sides can make a rebuttal and surrebuttal, the court must consider three motions filed by the defense to find Manning not guilty on Exceeding Authorized Access, Aiding the Enemy, and Stealing USG Property. As a procedural matter, Fein directs Lind to consider these three motions in a "light most favorable to the prosecution."

Judge Lind denies each of the three motions.

REBUTTAL

The government requests to recall two previous witnesses, Jihrleah Showman and Special Agent David Shaver.

OVERGAARD Ms. McNamara said the accused told her, "I can apply what I learned to provide information to my officers and commanders and hopefully save lives." The government would like to offer what Ms. Showman said the accused said to her. It directly rebuts that the accused had some noble motive. It shows Manning's pre-deployment state of mind in the same time period he spoke with Ms. McNamara.

The United States also requests to recall Special Agent Shaver to discuss WikiLeaks tweets found on Manning's personal computer to rebut the evidence offered by the defense that WikiLeaks was considered and operated as a journalistic organization.

truth
US
US
OVE

HURLEY It's not as though they first heard Professor Benkler's testimony on the stand. Ma'am, you're a sophisticated trier of fact. A panoply of evidence that the court can consider in making its findings already exists in the record, and there is no need to call a rebuttal witness for this.
HURLEY
The government even asks to call an "undetermined additional forensic investigator" to rebut Benkler's testimony.

LIND With respect to the government's intention to recall Special Agent Shaver: what's really relevant here is not whether WikiLeaks was a legitimate journalistic organization, it is whether Manning thought WikiLeaks was one. The court will allow it. But I'm not going to allow the government to call an additional forensic investigator witness to discuss the WikiLeaks Website. You had months to figure this out, government. We are at the last minute here.

JULY 18, 2013

The argument that Manning be found "not guilty" of stealing USG government property eventually leads Lind to allow an eleventh hour update to the charges Manning faces. The government charged that Manning stole databases. In the motion hearing, the defense argued that the soldier stole copies of information from databases.

COOMBS When we were asking for documents from Quantico, and we thought "documents" fairly encapsulated "e-mails," the government said no, no, no—words matter. If you wanted e-mails, you should have asked for e-mails. Words do matter. They matter the most when it's on a charge sheet. That's when words matter.

JULY 19, 2013

COOMBS Ms. McNamara testified about the fact that Manning exhibited concern and care for human life, that he was a humanist. Ms. Showman is going to testify to statements she alleges my client made only to her. Those statements do not rebut whether or not Manning is a humanist. For that, we don't believe it is proper rebuttal.

OVERGAARD The government objected to Ms. McNamara's testimony. The defense specifically stated they were offering it for motive of the accused. The defense elicited testimony contrary to what Ms. Showman will testify was the accused's motive. So the government is choosing now to call her back in rebuttal.

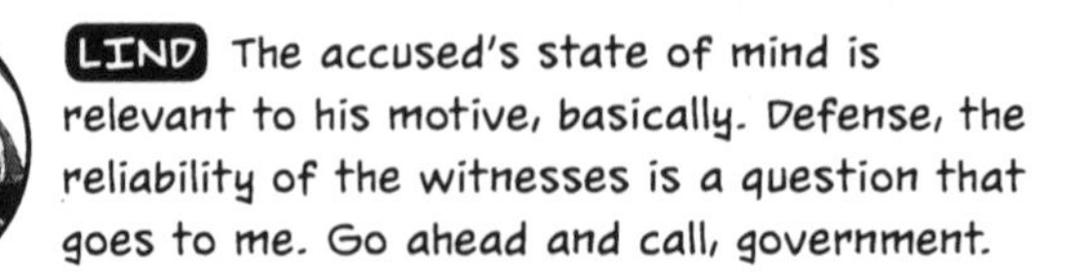

LIND The accused's state of mind is relevant to his motive, basically. Defense, the reliability of the witnesses is a question that goes to me. Go ahead and call, government.

A PERSONAL VENDETTA EMERGES

OVERGAARD Did you ever ask PFC Manning his motivation for joining the military?

SHOWMAN He indicated that he joined the military mainly for training and educational benefits. It was kind of an answer that every soldier gives. I wanted something a little bit more in-depth, so I tapped the flag on my shoulder and I asked him what the flag meant to him. He said the flag meant nothing to him. He did not consider himself to have allegiance to this country or any people.

Coombs cross-examines Showman.

COOMBS You got very upset at the time that he made these statements?

SHOWMAN As an American and as a fellow soldier, I was distraught.

WITNESS

COOMBS Why didn't you reduce the alleged disloyal statements to writing?

SHOWMAN As a leader, I had reached my limitation. I had handed off the issue to my superior. Sergeant Adkins said he would take care of it.

COOMBS I want to concentrate on the facts that you rely upon to say he was a possible spy.

SHOWMAN He would handle tasks very enthusiastically. Any time you tried to pull him off of that task, especially if it was a computer task, he would appear to be very flustered and not really function properly after that. It just wasn't normal for someone that should be handling classified information.

COOMBS Let's stop there then. What made that, in your mind, say "this is a possible spy"?

SHOWMAN It was honestly a feeling in my gut more than anything. It didn't appear as though he truly believed in what it meant to be a soldier. I did my duty by going to my superiors.

Showman makes no secret of her antagonism towards Manning. The former supervisor admits to calling Manning "faggoty"—for not being able to do many pushups. Between her first testimony at the Article 32 hearing in December 2011 and the trial, she sat down in an interview for the documentary *We Steal Secrets: The Story of WikiLeaks*, describing an episode where, in a separate incident, Manning retaliated. Coombs plays video for the court.

I couldn't believe he messed with me. I literally have 15-inch biceps. I'm probably the last person he should have punched.

SURREBUTTAL

COOMBS Did Specialist Showman ever report to you that Manning told her the American flag meant nothing to him?

ADKINS I don't recall . . . and I don't remember.

COOMBS That she believed that Manning was a spy?

ADKINS I, I don't recall and I . . . don't remember, sir.

Answering the questions very slowly, Adkins reveals he's been diagnosed with memory loss, having suffered a fall on a tour in Iraq in 2004. Coombs presses on, emphasizing the absence of a written document for the incident Showman described.

COOMBS In this case, did you ever see a written counseling statement regarding any alleged disloyal comments by my client?

ADKINS I don't recall having seen one, sir.

COOMBS Do you recall ever addressing any disloyal statements regarding Manning at any time?

ADKINS Well, after he was arrested, but before that, no.

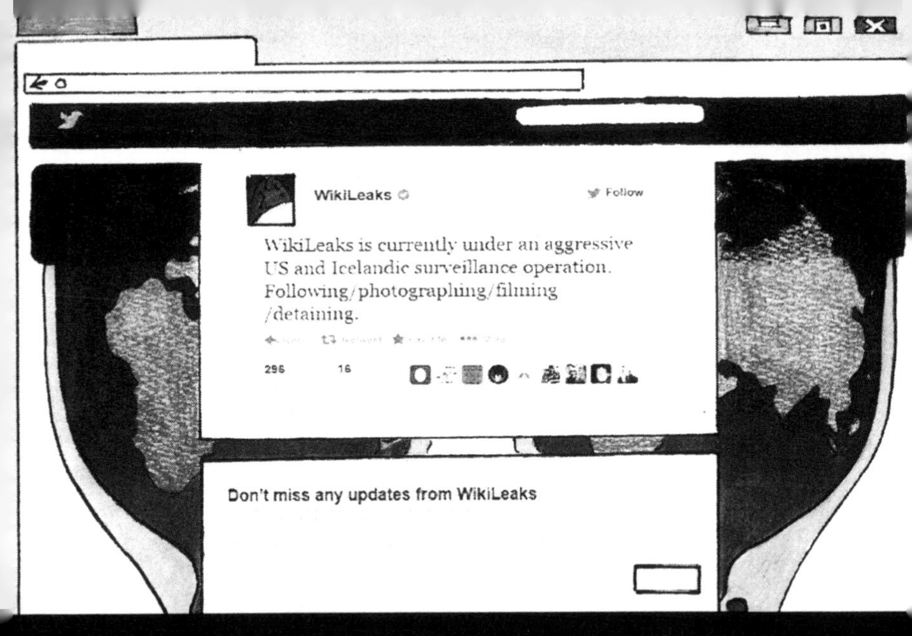
WikiLeaks
Follow
WikiLeaks is currently under an aggressive US and Icelandic surveillance operation. Following/photographing/filming /detaining.
296
16
Don't miss any updates from WikiLeaks

The government submitted this tweet to rebut the idea that WikiLeaks is a legitimate journalistic institution.

TOOMAN I guess we're presuming that the government thinks that if WikiLeaks is under surveillance, then they are not a legitimate journalistic organization. To rebut that we have three records pulled from the FBI vault: of Mike Wallace and Ernest Hemingway, as well as Paul Harvey. They refer to these individuals as journalists. Clearly the United States does investigations or surveillance on important legitimate members of the media and journalists.

FEIN It's in the hands or the eyes of Manning. That's why we contested Professor Benkler's relevance from the get-go. We're offering it to show that Manning knew it was not a legitimate news organization based on the evidence that was in front of him—not, in general, whether it was or was not.

JULY 25, 2013

CLOSING ARGUMENTS

The government begins an aggressive and often repetitive closing argument sustained over seven hours, winning the day's news cycle.

FEIN

FEIN Bradley Manning swore an oath of allegiance to protect the national security of the United States. He deployed to a war zone fully armed, not only with a rifle, but with the stark knowledge of the harm that could accrue if classified materials were compromised. His mission, as an intelligence analyst, was a special trust. Within weeks of arriving in Iraq, he destroyed this trust with the indiscriminate compromise of hundreds of thousands of classified documents. He delivered these documents for notoriety.

Manning's work as an intelligence analyst demonstrates he knew and appreciated the types of information he deliberately chose to compromise. He wantonly caused intelligence to be published on the Internet.

FEIN Manning aided the enemy of the United States by knowingly giving intelligence through indirect means to al-Qaeda. Manning pulled as much information as possible, to please Julian Assange, in order to get that information released. He knew that WikiLeaks' goals and methods were different than anything that could be characterized as traditional journalism.
Why did Manning choose WikiLeaks? Because they sought, almost exclusively from the United States, classified information to disclose in the name of transparency information anarchy. The United States has not made these documents available to the public. They were closely held.
Manning knew that it must also be presumed that foreign adversaries will review any sensitive or classified information posted to WikiLeaks. The Apache video documents the actions and experiences of U.S. service members conducting a wartime mission. Although the Apache video is not classified, it's sensitive. Manning thought the video was cool and decided to release it to a bunch of anti-government activists and anarchists to achieve maximum exposure and advance his personal quest for notoriety.
US
US
FEIN

FEIN The theme here is Manning's consistently cavalier attitude towards this material.

The publication of the Detainee Assessment Briefs deprived the United States of the exclusive possession and use of that information. Instead of helping his unit, Manning took the opportunity to harvest over 250,000 Department of State cables for release. Manning thought he was smart enough to know what's going on in the world.

His actions are not those of a person trying to spark a national debate but rather of a soldier no longer loyal to his country because he had no national interest at heart. Manning never once mentioned protecting the American public or the United States as motivation for his crimes. Manning did have a general evil intent, manifested through his deliberate and repeated compromise of classified information.

Officials raided Osama bin Laden's compound and collected a letter from bin Laden to a member of al-Qaeda requesting the Department of State cables posted to WikiLeaks. Media perception is important to al-Qaeda. Any event that places al-Qaeda in a positive light or U.S. forces in negative light is beneficial to them.

FEIN Manning was an anarchist whose agenda was made abundantly clear almost immediately after he deployed to Iraq. He was not naive.

The United States is confident that after reviewing all of the evidence, you will find him guilty beyond a reasonable doubt of all the charges. Manning was not a humanist. He was a hacker. He was not a troubled young soul. He was a determined soldier with the knowledge, ability, and desire to harm the United States. He was not a whistle-blower.

He was a traitor.

truth
truth
truth
truth
FEIN

JULY 26, 2013

COOMBS When you don't know somebody well, what do you do to find out the truth? A good indicator is what that person says at a time which they think nobody is ever going to see the words they have said or wrote down.

In the months leading up to deployment Manning was trying to apply his knowledge to hopefully save lives. He tells Ms. McNamara so. He has no reason to lie to her.

Another very good indication of the true nature of Manning: the chat with Adrian Lamo prior to his arrest. He's concerned that he's made a mess. He's reached out to Lamo for moral support because of their common background. Lamo testified that he thought this man was young, idealistic and well-intentioned.

His feeling of being connected to other people, that we have a duty to each other as humans—what a great thing for a young man to feel. That is not anti-patriotic. That is not anti-American.

What was his motive? Nowhere does he discuss, "I know the enemy is going to get this." He's solely concentrated on making a difference, changing the way the world operates.

COOMBS In the deployed environment, the only way you can do your job is to read this intelligence disengaged. But he's troubled by what he sees: these are real people dying. "Targets." That's how you talk about people in order to not be concerned that you are killing them.

Certainly you could view that video from the standpoint of the Apache crew engaging an enemy. You also can view that from the standpoint of a young person looking at what we now know to be the truth: two reporters just standing in a group on a street corner. Shot like fish in a barrel.

What do you do when you can't disengage? What do you do when these images are burned into your mind? When the court looks at this, the defense requests that you not disengage. Did they all deserve to die? That is what Manning is seeing and questioning.

DTY
660
174

COOMBS The government's story has the logic of a child. There's no sophistication there—just taking facts and running with them.

The 2009 WikiLeaks Most Wanted List—the government tried to make this an evil thing. But it was WikiLeaks saying, "Tell us, humanitarians, activists, fellow reporters, what in your country is being hidden that you believe the public should know? We are going to work to obtain it." What does this sound like? Journalism.

To add insult to injury, they put up the testimony of Specialist Showman, relying on her to portray my client as disloyal. She apparently had this exchange with Manning—just never reduced to writing—where he said he had no loyalty to the country or the American flag. Then after Manning is arrested, and she knows why he's arrested, she never mentions it. She has this incredible story of telling Sergeant Adkins that Manning is a possible spy. Why would she make up this story? Because she's got room to fabricate. She doesn't like Manning.

Mr. Adkins doesn't remember her telling him any of this. He never wrote about the alleged statements—something you would expect. And apparently this person who has no loyalty to the country or flag is one of his unit's go-to-analysts.

COOMBS The amount of the documents in this case actually is the best evidence that he was discrete in what he chose. If he were "systematically harvesting," we would be talking about millions of documents.

The emperor has no clothes. Manning chose items that we should know but would not cause damage to the United States.

Certainly there are secrets that could gravely impact our country. Manning had access to those. This too speaks to Manning's selectivity.

truth
truth

Look at the Farah video: the government didn't prove that Manning was the source. For Wget, you have to *knowingly* exceed your authorized access—there can't be an implicit access restriction. There's no restriction on downloading from the Net-Centric Diplomacy Database. We have a wealth of information that shows what was and was not prohibited was subject to who you asked. They did not prove that Manning stole the charged databases: what Manning took was a copy of those records. Everyone testified that SigActs are historical documents. Manning understood that.

COOMBS If the army didn't know that the enemy went to WikiLeaks, how could Manning have known? Then the government argues: We must presume that the enemy would go to any source on the Internet to find information. This is a negligence argument. In Manning's instance, giving something to a legitimate news organization is the way we hold our government accountable.

He never discussed wanting to get information to the enemy. All the forensics prove his motive was to spark reforms. He did not have a general evil intent.

Is Manning somebody who is a traitor, had no loyalty to this country and wanted to systematically harvest as much information as possible for his true employer, WikiLeaks? Is that what the evidence shows? Or is he a young, naive soldier with good intentions, with his humanist beliefs central to his decisions, whose sole thought was, "Maybe I just can make a difference." It's clear what the truth is in this case. We are hoping that the court sees that as well.

The gallery erupts.
Free Bradley Manning!
Free Brad!
Thank you,
Brad, you're a
Free
Thank you, Brad!
LIND All right. That's enough.
the gallery, this is a court of law. I
please, that you keep your reaction

The prosecution gets the final word.

FEIN A typical whistle-blower would find something, take it up through their chain of command to their team leader, their squad leader, take to the chaplain, to a Judge Advocate General, to an Inspector General, to another government official. That's what a whistle-blower does. Manning did not care about anyone but himself. He betrayed every solider who relied on him.

He knew the scope of his actions. He knew the size of his audience. He wanted the world to see the information he compromised. He was right, because even Osama bin Laden saw it.

Private First Class Manning voluntarily embraced a higher duty when he swore an oath to defend this country and his fellow soldiers. Instead, he compromised hundreds of thousands of documents. That is the general evil intent and that is aiding the enemy.

US
FEIN

JULY 30, 2013

VERDICT
LIND I will now announce the verdict. If there are any outbursts or disturbing conduct I will stop, and I will order the disturbing party escorted out of the courtroom by security. Accused and counsel, please rise.

LIND Private First Class Bradley Manning, this court finds you:

Aiding the Enemy: NOT GUILTY

Wanton Publication of Intelligence: GUILTY

Violation of the Espionage Act ("Collateral Murder"):
in accordance with your plea, GUILTY to lesser-included offenses

Violation of the Espionage Act (CIA Red Cell Memos): GUILTY

Stealing USG Property (Iraq War Logs): GUILTY

Violation of the Espionage Act (Iraq War Logs): GUILTY

Stealing USG Property (Afghan War Diaries): GUILTY

Violation of the Espionage Act (Afghan War Diaries): GUILTY

Stealing USG Property (Gitmo Detainee Briefs): GUILTY

Violation of the Espionage Act (Gitmo Detainee Briefs): GUILTY

Violation of the Espionage Act (Farah Records): GUILTY

Violation of the Espionage Act (Garani Airstike Video): NOT GUILTY

Stealing USG Property (Cablegate): GUILTY

Violation of Computer Fraud Abuse Act "Exceeding Authorized Access" (Cablegate): GUILTY

(Reykjavik 13):
in accordance with your plea, GUILTY to lesser-included offenses

Violation of the Espionage Act (2008 USACIC Memo): GUILTY

Stealing USG Property (Global Address List): GUILTY

Attempting to Bypass Network Security Mechanism: GUILTY

Adding Unauthorized Software (1): GUILTY

Adding Unauthorized Software (2): GUILTY

Using an Information System Other than Intended: GUILTY

Wrongfully Storing Classified Information,
in accordance with your plea, GUILTY

TED STATES
LIND Please be seated.

JULY 31, 2013

TO HOW MANY YEARS WILL MANNING BE SENTENCED?

In the sentencing phase, trial counsel can now present "evidence as to any aggravating circumstances directly relating or resulting from" Manning's release of documents to WikiLeaks. The prosecution's first witness is Brigadier General Robert Carr.

CARR As a result of the Afghan logs, I only know of one individual that was killed. The individual was an Afghan national who had a relationship with the United States government. The Taliban came out publicly and said that they killed him as a result of him being associated with the information in these logs. We went back and searched for this individual's name in all of the disclosures. The name was not there. The name of the individual that was killed was not in the disclosures. So no, I don't have a specific example of somebody who died as a result of this.

LIND I'm going to disregard any testimony about the Taliban killing somebody in accordance with the leak.

AUGUST 1, 2013

The government calls State Department witnesses to testify that the released cables had what they repeatedly call a "chilling effect" on . . .

Diplomatic relations in the Middle East and North Africa:

ELIZABETH DIBBLE Horror and disbelief that our diplomatic communications had been released and were available on public Websites for the world to see.

In Latin America:

JOHN FEELEY There are an awful lot of people in Latin America who have very mixed feelings about the United States and see the United States as more of a neo-liberal imperial presence. Our soft power, quite frankly, is something that we consciously want to work on and develop as opposed to hard military power.

AUGUST 2, 2013

Within the State Department:

SUSAN SWART The belief was that the people that were vetted to be on classified systems understood the rules for handling classified information. After the WikiLeaks incident you couldn't just believe that it's a trusted individual.

And on the Department's credibility:

MICHAEL KOZAK I would say that the greatest damage is that for people coming in and talking to us and trying to work with us to promote the advance of human rights and democracy in their countries. It's created a chilling effect on people. They can't be sure now that what they say to us is going to stay confidential, or whether it's going to get broadcast around.

The government elicits only generalities before moving to closed sessions for each witness to give specifics.

AUGUST 5, 2013

"The damage continues to roll out," the highest-profile witness, Undersecretary of State for Management Patrick F. Kennedy, testified. "People have long memories."

During cross-examination, Coombs plays a video clip of Robert Gates, secretary of defense at the time of the releases:

GATES I have heard the impact of these releases on our foreign policy described as a meltdown, as a game-changer and so on. I think those descriptions are fairly significantly overwrought. We are still essentially the indispensable nation.

Is this embarrassing? Yes. Is it awkward? Yes. Consequences for U.S. foreign policy? I think fairly modest.

AUGUST 6, 2013

Honoring the defense's near constant objections to the State Department witnesses' testimony, Judge Lind limits the scope of testimony on the alleged chilling effect to periods directly following the releases.

> "Many so-called ills of the world are laid at my client's feet," Coombs argued. "In diplomacy, there are so many factors that come to play in relationships."

Judge Lind also grants a defense motion to combine sixteen charges into eight, reducing Manning's maximum sentence from 136 years to 90.

FEIN How would you characterize your relationship and our relationship with the Pakistani military? Was it a positive one?

Major General Michael Nagata:

NAGATA Not perfect, not without problems and friction, but it was definitely a positive trajectory.

FEIN Do you recall becoming aware that purported Department of State information had been released publicly in November and December 2010?

NAGATA I do indeed.

FEIN Without disclosing classified information in an open session, did you observe any impact to the mission in this timeframe as a result of the releases?

NAGATA I did.

FEIN We would move to a closed session at this time.

AUGUST 8, 2013

The government calls Commander Youssef Aboul-Enein, a specialist in militant Islamist ideology and adjunct professor at National Defense University, to testify on two instances where Al Qaeda used the WikiLeaks releases.

WINTER 1431 2011

INSPIRE

ABOUL-ENEIN The first was in *Inspire Magazine.* The second was a video. What you find is great propaganda value for al Qaeda. What they've extrapolated out of that is a message that the United States is hypocritical, that it does not value life and it does not particularly value Iraqi or Muslim life.

Also very powerful from al Qaeda's perspective is the image of that young boy that was in the van. Of course, luckily, he survived the attack, but then they show the young boy and his scars. What al Qaeda is able to portray is: not only does the United States not value life, but this could be your child. "When are you going to understand and join our cause, and be sympathetic to our cause" is their message in that video.

HURLEY Has al Qaeda or al Qaeda in the Arabian Peninsula claimed any tactical successes because of the information acquired from WikiLeaks?
ABOUL-ENEIN No.

AUGUST 9, 2013

Rear Admiral Kevin Donegan:

DONEGAN There was absolutely impact as a result of the release of those cables.
We had to inform these people their name was on this and, therefore, the enemy likely had access to knowing they were a source to the United States and they would likely be in danger. This was not a small operation. There is not a street address that we can go to. It's not simple to find an individual so that increases risk in these operations. You're not walking up to a door in the street saying, "Hey, Mr. Smith, want you to know your name is on the list."

Major General Kenneth F. Mckenzie:

MCKENZIE Long-term collective security is based on reassuring your allies. It is fundamental to U.S. long-term strategic interests that we maintain a positive, two-way relationship with these nations.

AUGUST 12, 2013

The defense's phase of the sentencing proceedings brought officers from Manning's unit to testify. Coombs elicited testimony to demonstrate that the army kept Manning as an intelligence analyst even as they missed behavioral signs that Manning faced mental health problems, including those related to struggling with his gender.

Colonel David Miller:

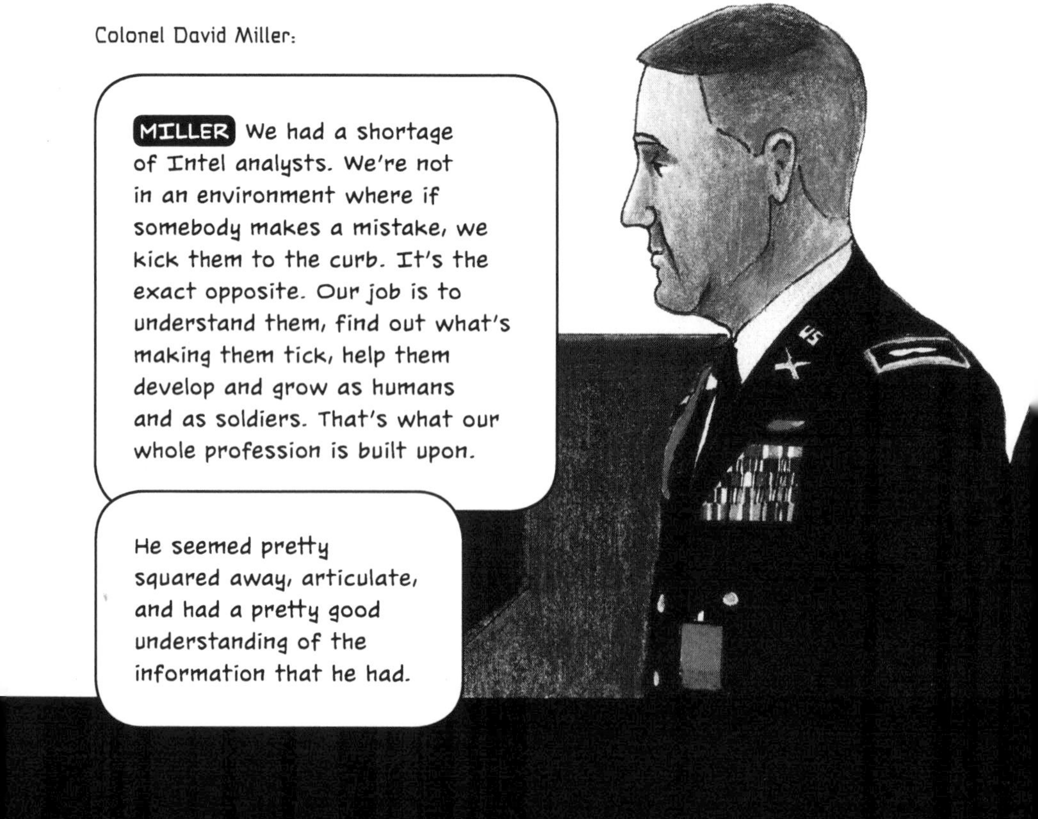

MILLER We had a shortage of Intel analysts. We're not in an environment where if somebody makes a mistake, we kick them to the curb. It's the exact opposite. Our job is to understand them, find out what's making them tick, help them develop and grow as humans and as soldiers. That's what our whole profession is built upon.

He seemed pretty squared away, articulate, and had a pretty good understanding of the information that he had.

"There was pressure on the whole unit to deploy," Major Clifford Clausen testified. Six other officers testified to a lack of authority in Manning's unit, as Coombs builds the case that in an important way, the army failed Manning.

AUGUST 13, 2013

Paul Adkins returns to the stand again to testify why he failed to report Manning's emerging gender dysphoria up the chain of command in a timely manner. Over one month passed before bringing to his superiors' attention a photograph of Manning as a woman, which the soldier attached to an email to Adkins titled "My problem."

ADKINS I really didn't think at the time that having a picture floating around of one of my soldiers in drag was in the best interests of the intel mission. I thought that was being handled by his therapist.

Lillian Smith is a government-appointed information assurance expert hired to assist the defense.

SMITH I reviewed the initial investigation to see if any specific information assurance violations or failures had occurred that enabled Manning to do what he did. I noted that there were several instances where soldiers had voiced their concern over Manning's erratic behavior before and during the deployment, and others documented conduct prior to and during the deployment that should have raised red flags.

Things weren't being done in accordance with the regulation as far as how to handle removable media. It was an undisciplined environment when it came to compliance. I would have expected the unit to take some action to discipline those that were not following the regulation to ensure that information assurance practices were being enforced. Trust, but verify. When we do that then we preclude classified information from being compromised.
STAFF

Two military psychologists unpack Manning's behavior in the context of his diagnosed gender dysphoria, the deployment atmosphere and the military at large under "Don't ask, don't tell."

Captain Dr. Michael Worsley treated Manning at FOB Hammer, including a late night session following the incident where he hit Showman.

WORSLEY He was having issues at work and he explained the outburst. He brought up in therapy this issue of identity, questioning how he could be himself. Being deployed is very isolating. Being an intel person working with top-secret clearance is even more isolating.

Being in the military and having a gender identity issue do not exactly go hand-in-hand—it further serves to isolate. He finally felt much more comfortable just having it out. But there would never be a time that he would be able to be openly female in the military.

Prior to his testimony, Captain Dr. David Moulton, a forensic psychologist, reviewed Manning's case. He interviewed Manning extensively, examined his medial records, interviews with family and peers, school records, and reports from a social worker assigned to Manning.

MOULTON He has gender dysphoria, otherwise known as gender identity disorder. Gender is very much a core of our identity as individuals. When that is off keel it can cause a lot of stress and depression.

Manning was very interested in doing his duty and especially interested in getting his GI Bill. Manning is intelligent and desired to get a college education, but had a lot of socioeconomic limitations.

He's got chronic stressors as well. He was raised by alcoholic parents and took care of his severely alcoholic mother.

At the time of the alleged offenses he was under severe emotional distress. Conversations and interviews all fit in with his system of beliefs. Historically, Manning has been pretty true to his principles.

Following expert witnesses, Casey Manning gives a portrait of her younger sibling's childhood.

CASEY MANNING My dad was a functional alcoholic. My mother would drink hard liquor at least every day. It usually started off pretty early. It was continuous until she passed out or went to bed. She couldn't or wouldn't get up. In the middle of the night I would get up and make a bottle for Brad, change his diaper, rock him back to sleep. I took care of him.

My dad told my mom he was leaving and my mom took a full bottle of Valium, and then she was drinking heavily at that time. In the car on the way to the hospital, my 12-year-old brother had to go back there and make sure his mom was still breathing. They pumped her stomach. She was admitted into the psychiatric ward. Dad left. She came back home.

One night she had been drinking heavily. She had come at me. I put up my hands defensively and pushed her. Since she was so drunk, she fell over and hit her tailbone. She was lying on the floor. I turned and Brad was right there. He had seen the whole thing. She's screaming profanities at me, saying, "Don't touch me." Then just a few minutes later I could hear her calling Brad. She wanted him to get her drink from the table. "Don't get her a drink," I said. "You can either stay in your room and ignore her or you can come up in my room and sleep on the floor." He chose to sleep on the floor that night. The next day she asked me to leave.

WITNESS

CASEY MANNING My brother, about six months old. We were living in the hotel in Phoenix. I found a box, and I was scooting him around on the floor, and he was playing in it.
That was my senior prom. My mom and little brother and my dad. She had probably had a little bit to drink.
That's one of his grade school photos.
That's my brother in the front area of the pasture.
That was out in the pasture on the swing set swinging.

That was my room, and he was hanging out in there playing on the saddle I had.

Him playing on the computer. If he wasn't at the computer, he was in his room playing Legos.

That's my wedding in Vegas December of '04.

That was Thanksgiving '06. Our Aunt Debbie's house.

CASEY MANNING It's amazing how much he has matured. I just hope he can be who he wants to be. I hope he can just be happy.

In one of the rare moments when Manning speaks at length in court, he reads an apology.

MANNING I'm sorry that my actions hurt people. I'm sorry that it hurt the United States. At the time of my decisions, as you know, I was dealing with a lot of issues, issues that are ongoing, and they are continuing to affect me. Although they have caused me considerable difficulty in my life, these issues are not an excuse for my actions.

I understood what I was doing and the decisions I made. I did not truly appreciate the broader effects of my actions. Those effects are clear to me now through both self-reflection during my confinement and through the merits of sentencing testimony I have seen here. When I made these decisions, I believed I was going to help people, not hurt people. In retrospect I should have worked more aggressively inside the system.

MANNING I can only go forward. Before I can do that, I understand that I must pay a price for my decisions. I hope to one day live in a manner that I haven't been able to in the past. I want to go to college, to get a degree and to have a meaningful relationship with my sister, with my sister's family and my family.
I hope that you can give me the opportunity to prove, not through words, but through conduct, that I am a good person and that I can return to a productive place in society.
MANN

The defense's last sentencing witness takes the stand. She is Debra Van Alstyne, Manning's aunt.

DEBRA VAN ALSTYNE He understands now that there are people who love him and care about him. I'm not sure he was really convinced of that before. That's a big change. Seems like at some point he can go out and have a good life and get his education and do the things that he really wants to do. I think he's got a lot to contribute.
I just hope that she takes into account that he had a very hard start to his life. He worked very hard. He's a good person. He cares about people.

AUGUST 20, 2013

THE GOVERNMENT'S MESSAGE: WHISTLEBLOWERS BEWARE

MORROW There may not be a soldier in the history of the United States Army who displayed such an extreme disregard for the judgment of the officers appointed above him and the orders of the president of the United States. He created a grave risk of harm to national security and endangered the well-being of innocent civilians and soldiers.

The United States asks you to sentence Manning to forfeit all pay allowances, to pay the United States a fine of $100,000, to be reduced to Private E1, to be confined for no less than 60 years and to be dishonorably discharged from the service.

He betrayed the United States and deserves to spend the majority of his remaining life in confinement. There is value in deterrence. This court must send a message to any soldier contemplating stealing classified information. Punish Manning's actions.

COOMBS Our system has evolved from a punishment-only viewpoint. Certainly Manning took the very first step towards rehabilitation: he accepted responsibility. Society's interest is in restoring this man to a productive place. Look at the reality of the situation. We are out of Iraq and on our way out of Afghanistan. Guantanamo, if the president has his way, will be closed. Diplomacy, we know, continues.

Sixty years. It's only when you put it in context that you truly understand how wrong it would be to give that sentence. Sixty years is almost three times the length of Manning's life. It's longer than any of the parties here today have been alive.

What was happening in 1953? That's how long the government wants Manning to sit in jail, and that would be wrong.

COOMBS This young man now sits before you three years wiser, three years in confinement. Some of that confinement, as the court has determined, was unlawful. Where others might have broken, he didn't. His resilience makes him a prime candidate to be restored to society. We should not rob him of his youth.
The defense requests that you adjudge a sentence that allows him to have a life.

AUGUST 21, 2013

LIND The accused and counsel, please rise.

Bradley E. Manning, this court sentences you to be reduced to the grade of Private E1, to forfeit all pay and allowances, to be confined for 35 years and to be dishonorably discharged from the service.

Please be seated. Manning will be credited with 1,182 days of pre-trial confinement and 112 days of credit, for a total of 1,294 days of sentence credit. This court is adjourned.

BAILIFF All rise.
LIND Carry on.

USDB
U.S. DISCIPLINARY BARRACKS
FORT LEAVENWORTH KANSAS

J.R.C.F.

AT THE PRESS CONFERENCE THAT AFTERNOON

COOMBS Next week, I will file on behalf of my client a request to the secretary of the army that the president pardon PFC Manning, or at the very least commute his sentence to time served. I want to share with you PFC Manning's statement, which is part of that request:

The decisions that I made in 2010 were made out of concern for my country and the world that we live in. Since the tragic events of 9/11, our country has been at war.

It was not until I was in Iraq reading secret military reports on a daily basis that I started to question the morality of what we were doing. It was at this time that I realized that in our efforts to meet the risk posed to us by the enemy, we had forgotten our humanity. We consciously elected to devalue human life both in Iraq and Afghanistan. When we engaged those that we perceived were the enemy, we sometimes killed innocent civilians. Whenever we killed innocent civilians, instead of accepting responsibility for our conduct we elected to hide behind the veil of national security and classified information, in order to avoid any public accountability.

PARDON
BRADLEY
ARDON
RADLEY

In our zeal to kill the enemy, we internally debated the definition of torture. We held individuals at Guantanamo for years without due process. We inexplicably turned a blind eye to torture and executions by the Iraqi government. And we stomached countless other acts in the name of our War on Terror.

Patriotism is often the cry sold when morally questionable acts are advocated by those in power. When these cries of patriotism drown out any logically-based dissension, it is usually the American solider who is given the order to carry out some ill-conceived mission.

Our nation has had similar dark moments for the virtues of democracy: the Trail of Tears, the Dred Scott decision, McCarthyism, and the Japanese-American internment camps, to name a few. I am confident that many of the actions since 9/11 will one day be viewed in a similar light.

As the late Howard Zinn once said, "There is not a flag large enough to cover the shame of killing innocent people."

I understand that my actions violated the law. I regret if my actions hurt anyone or harmed the United States. I only wanted to help people. When I chose to disclose classified information, I did so out of a love for my country, and a sense of duty to others.

If you deny my request for a pardon, I will serve my time knowing that sometimes you have to pay a heavy price to live in a free society. I will gladly pay that price if it means we could have a country conceived in liberty, dedicated to the proposition that all women and men are created equal.

Epilogue

On August 22, 2013, the day after her sentencing, Coombs appeared on *Today* to announce Pvt. Manning's desire to live her life as a woman. Here is her statement, "The Next Stage of My Life," in full:

> I want to thank everybody who has supported me over the last three years. Throughout this long ordeal, your letters of support and encouragement have helped keep me strong. I am forever indebted to those who wrote to me, made a donation to my defense fund, or came to watch a portion of the trial. I would especially like to thank Courage to Resist and the Bradley Manning Support Network for their tireless efforts in raising awareness for my case and providing for my legal representation.
>
> As I transition into this next phase of my life, I want everyone to know the real me. I am Chelsea Manning. I am a female. Given the way that I feel, and have felt since childhood, I want to begin hormone therapy as soon as possible. I hope that you will support me in this transition. I also request that, starting today, you refer to me by my new name and use the feminine pronoun (except in official mail to the confinement facility). I look forward to receiving letters from supporters and having the opportunity to write back.

TODAY EXCLUSIVE
WHAT'S NEXT FOR BRADLEY MANNING?
ATTORNEY: CLIENT TO LIVE LIFE AS A WOMAN

A spokeswoman confirmed to journalists that Ft. Leavenworth does not offer hormone replacement therapy. In a memo to the Private Manning Support Network, Manning has indicated that, with help from David Coombs, she will seek access to treatment first by "administrative remedies" and then, if necessary, by litigation.

Manning has been placed in "general population", meaning she is able to participate in all vocational and educational opportunities. She is also allowed to receive visitors and correspondence.

Mail must be addressed exactly as follows:
Bradley E. Manning 89289
1300 North Warehouse Road
Fort Leavenworth, Kansas 66027-2304

While envelopes and money orders must be addressed to "Bradley E. Manning," Chelsea prefers her chosen name be used on the inside of letters. She is currently eligible to receive mail, including birthday (December 17) or holiday cards, money orders, and cashiers checks. You are also permitted to mail unframed photographs not larger than 5" x 7". Letters should be limited to six physical pages. All mail will be inspected upon arrival. Any mail that is considered detrimental to security, good order, discipline, or the correctional mission of the USDB will be rejected. Do not send cash, jewelry, compact discs, electronics, or other items of value with your correspondence. You are also not permitted to send newspapers, periodicals, magazines or books. If you want to send a specific book or other reading material to Chelsea, you must do so by having those items sent directly from the publisher. You may also not send anything that violates postal regulations or contains obscenity, blackmail, contraband or threats.

To get involved, learn more, or donate to the Private Manning Support Network, visit www.privatemanning.org.

Donate to her legal defense:

Manning has asked Coombs to continue representing her. He plans to see to it that she spends her confinement free of cruel and unusual punishment and receives hormone replacement therapy.

Send a check with the memo "Chelsea Manning Defense" to:
Law Office of David E. Coombs, 11 South Angell Street, #317, Providence, RI, 02906

Thank you . . .

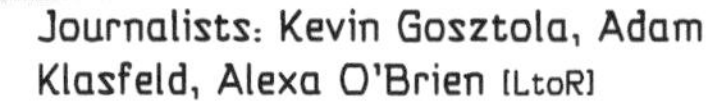

Journalists: Kevin Gosztola, Adam Klasfeld, Alexa O'Brien [LtoR]

Media sketch artist: William Hennessy

PRESIDENT OBAMA
PARDON
BRADLEY

Private Manning Support Network: Jeff Paterson, Emma Cape, Nathan Fuller [LtoR]

and to Amanda Bartlett, Andrew Blake, Barbara Bridges, Cathie Phelps, Chase Madar, David Dishneau, David and Tanya Coombs, David Powell, Debra Van Poolen, Ed Pilkington, Farah Muhsin Al Mousawi, Gerry Condon, Janet Wilson, Josh Tooman, Julia Macedo, Julian Assange, Julie Tate, Karen Steele, Kay Rudin, Liz Wahl, Matt Sledge, Michael Thurman, Mike McKee, Mom & Dad, Molly Crabapple, Nancy Bacci, Owen Wiltshire, Patrick Semansky, Rainey Reitman, Robert and Grace Brune, Sarah Harrison, Steve Rhodes, Tom and April Hurley, Vaughan Smith, Vlad Teichberg, Wylie Stecklow, William Wagner, Xeni Jardin, Yoni Miller, Zack Pesavento, and everyone at OR Books: Colin, Courtney, Emily, Justin, Max and Natasha.